SLUGGY FREELANCE

BOOK 7

A VERY BIG BANG!

by
PETE ABRAMS

SLUGGY FREELANCE

Sluggy Freelance #7 - A Very Big Bang! is an original publication of Pete Abrams and is published by Plan Nine Publishing.

ISBN 1-929462-49-2
First Printing July 2002

 For information on this book and other *Sluggy Freelance* titles, please go to our web site or write to:

Plan Nine
Publishing

1237 Elon Place
High Point, NC 27263
336.454.7766
www.plan9.org

Bringing you the future tomorrow, but what's funny today!

Printed in China

TO JOE-JOE-JOEFOTRON!

To Joe "Sunday" Horton! For being a colorist beyond compare and a great friend. *Or the other way around!* ;)

Also by Pete Abrams

Is It Not Nifty?
Worship the Comic
When Holidays Attack
Game Called on Account of Naked Chick
Yippie Skippy, The Evil!
The Bug, the Witch, and the Robot
Bastard Operator from Hell (illustrator)

guide to the sluggy freelance universe...

KIKI: HAPPY FERRET
NOTE: easily excitable.

DR. SCHLOCK: INFLATABLE TECH SCIENTIST FROM PARALLEL FUTURE
NOTE: Questionable motives.

CRYSTAL: LOCAL BARTENDER

SASHA: "UP-EX" DELIVERY GIRL

RIFF: FREELANCE BUM, INVENTOR

PET

DATING

HAVEN'T MET

AYLEE: ALIEN SECRETARY
NOTE: Changes form when immersed in a new environment.

GWYNN: UNEMPLOYED
NOTE: Recently rescued from demonic possession with the help of all of her friends.

MISTRUST

BROKE UP

BEST FRIENDS

YOU ARE HERE!

TORG'S SECRETARY

BEST FRIENDS

TORG: FREELANCE WEB DESIGNER

TORG LOVES ZOË

OASIS MADLY LOVES TORG

PET?

ZOË: COLLEGE CO-ED
NOTE: Has a magic tattoo that causes her to turn into a camel when the magic word is spoken aloud.

OASIS: GYMNASTIC ASSASSIN OF UNKNOWN ORIGIN

?

BUN-BUN: ANGRY BUNNY
NOTE: Has become the Easter Bunny by right of Caste. Wants desperately to shake that gig.

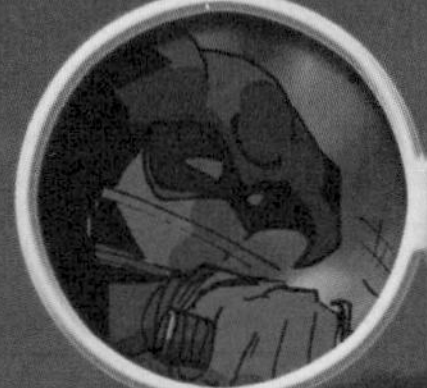

KUSARI: AGENT OF HERETI-CORP
NOTE: After Oasis for some reason.

WORK FOR BUN-BUN

BLACK OPS ELVES: EX-CHRISTMAS INFORMATION GATHERING ELVES
NOTE: Now working for Bun-bun.

BERT AND ANGELA: ONE'S AN ARTIST, BOTH ARE A LITTLE NUTTY
NOTE: Survived the horrors of Wispydale with Torg and Zoë previously.

NUDIST COLONIES ARE COOL.
YOU KNOW THE PROBLEM WITH NUDIST COLONIES?

NO QUALITY CONTROL.
POINT.

SO, HOW'S GWYNN DOING?
I FEEL LIKE I'M LIVING IN THIS SOAP OPERA! AND I'M STUCK IN THE MIDDLE OF IT!

WHAT'S GOING ON?
RIFF HASN'T TOLD GWYNN ABOUT SASHA YET!
IT'S NOT GWYNN'S BUSINESS WHO RIFF DATES.
HE LOOKS GUILTY!

OH! YOU THINK BY NOT TELLING GWYNN ABOUT SASHA, SASHA WILL THINK HE STILL HAS FEELINGS FOR GWYNN?
NO. SASHA DOESN'T MIND IF RIFF DOESN'T TELL GWYNN ABOUT HER.

WHY DOESN'T SASHA JUST TELL GWYNN?
SHE THINKS IT'S NOT HER PLACE TO INTERFERE. SHE'S JUST GO-ING TO AVOID GWYNN.

WAIT A MINUTE. IF SASHA'S OK WITH IT AND RIFF'S OK WITH IT, AND GWYNN DOESN'T KNOW ABOUT IT, WHAT'S THE BIG DEAL?
BY NOT BEING OPEN, ABOUT THEIR RELATIONSHIPS, IT LOOKS LIKE THEY HAVE SOMETHING TO HIDE!

HOW ARE YOU STUCK IN THE MIDDLE OF THIS AGAIN?
DO I HAVE TO START OVER FROM THE BEGINNING?
COULD YOU DRAW A FLOWCHART?

SIGN HERE...
... THANKS.

ZOË, YOU'VE GOT AN UP-EX DELIVERY FROM THE BUCKETS-O-CHEESE FACTORY!
DID SHE SAY ANYTHING?
DID WHO SAY WHAT?

HOW DID OPERATION "MAIL MYSELF CHEESE" GO?
SASHA DIDN'T IDENTIFY HERSELF TO GWYNN AT ALL! NOW, WHEN GWYNN FINDS OUT ABOUT HER, SHE'LL THINK SASHA WAS SNUBBING HER ON PURPOSE!

WHY DON'T YOU JUST TELL GWYNN WHO SHE IS?
I GUESS I COULD HAVE AT THE TIME, BUT AFTER ALL THAT'S HAPPENED...

SHE'LL THINK THAT *I* WAS KEEPING SASHA A SECRET FROM HER!
I FINISHED MY FLOWCHART!

JUST TELL ZOË I STOPPED BY WHEN SHE GETS BACK FROM CLASS, GWYNN!
WAIT A MINUTE, TORG! I WANTED TO THANK YOU!

FOR WHAT?
DETAILS ARE FOGGY, BUT I KNOW YOU GUYS PLAYED A BIG PART GETTING ME DEMON-FREE.

WELL, I WAS UNCONSCIOUS AT THE TIME, BUT YOU'RE WELCOME! HEY, CRYSTAL IS HOSTING "SURVIVOR NIGHT" AT THE BAR. WANT TO COME?

SURE! IS IT LIKE THE TELEVISION SHOW?
NO, YOU JUST HAVE TO SURVIVE THE DRINKS. IT USED TO BE KNOWN AS "CRYSTAL INVENTS NEW BEVERAGES NIGHT" UNTIL SHE MADE THAT DRINK OUT OF DRAMBUIE AND HAIR.
BLECK!

WHY DON'T YOU AND SASHA STOP BY SOME NIGHT TO WATCH A MOVIE WITH GWYNN AND ME?
CAN'T TONIGHT. I'VE GOT WORK TO DO, AND SASHA'S GOING TO HANG OUT WITH TORG AT THE BAR. IT'S "SURVIVOR NIGHT"!
FZZT!

WAIT... TORG INVITED GWYNN TO THE BAR TONIGHT!
LOOK, ZOË, TORG TOLD ME YOU'RE GETTING ALL HUNG UP ABOUT GWYNN AND SASHA MEETING...

TORG IS GETTING THEM TO MEET EACH OTHER!
Shrug

YOU DON'T THINK ANY-THING CAN GO WRONG WITH TORG TAKING MATTERS INTO HIS OWN HANDS?
I TOLD YOU ALREADY, I JUST DON'T THINK. IT'S POLICY!
FZZT!

IF YOU DON'T CARE, WHY DID YOU JUST WELD YOUR BELT-BUCKLE TO THIS THING?
UM... QUANTUM PHYSICS, YOU WOULDN'T UNDERSTAND.

TORG'S GOT SOMETHING UP HIS SLEEVE AND THAT CAN ONLY END IN DISASTER! I JUST HOPE I CAN GET TO THE BAR IN TIME!

MAYBE I'M THINKING ABOUT THIS TOO HARD. JUST BECAUSE I THINK GETTING GWYNN AND SASHA TOGETHER WILL CAUSE AN EXPLOSION, MAYBE TORG IS RIGHT AND IT'LL ACTUALLY DEFUSE THE SITUATION!

HI TORG!
HI, GWYNN! THIS IS SASHA, RIFF'S GIRL-FRIEND.

FIRE IN THE HOLE!

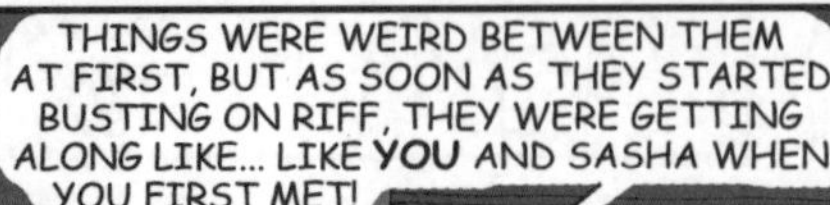

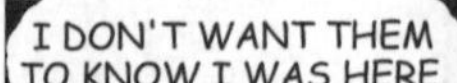

NOW THAT THE CHEESEBURGERITA HAS BEEN PROVEN TO MAKE GIRLS GET NAKED AND WEAR TABLECLOTHS, HAS ITS POSITION ON THE MENU BECOME GUARANTEED? OR WILL THE "HAPPY HEMORRHAGE" MAINTAIN THE LEAD?

FIND OUT ON THE NEXT

"CRYSTAL EXPERIMENTS WITH MIXED DRINKS SURVIVOR!"

EPISODE 52:

"DON'T LET CRYSTAL NEAR THE ISOTOPES"

HEY, REMEMBER THE "BOOK OF E-VILLE"?
THAT BOOK CONTAINING UNSPEAKABLE EVIL, OTHER THAN, AND INCLUDING, KIZKE HIMSELF? THE ONE KIZKE TOOK FROM ZOË AND ME IN THE PAST?

YES, BUT CHRONOLOGICALLY, THE LAST TIME I REMEMBER SEEING IT WAS WITH YOU ON TOP OF THE EMPIRE STATE BUILDING!
I THOUGHT **YOU** HAD IT! THAT WAS, LIKE, **YEARS** AGO!

WELL, ***SOMEBODY*** MUST HAVE PICKED IT UP!
I HOPE IT DIDN'T FALL INTO THE WRONG HANDS!

OH POWERFUL SHADOW, I SUMMON AND BIND THEE TO THIS MAGIC LOOKING CIRCLE-THINGY I DREW ON THE GROUND!

HEY, YOU KNOW THIS SOUNDED SUSPICIOUSLY LIKE A RECAP.
LET ME CHECK MY SCRIPT.

I AM SUMMONED!
COOL! IT WORKED!

WHAT KNOWLEDGE DO...**WHAT IS THAT SMELL?**

STRAWBERRIES? IS THAT **STRAWBERRIES?!?**

NERD-BOY ONLY KEEPS THOSE SCENTED AIR-FRESHENER CANDLES IN THE HOUSE.
AND WHERE IS THE CHICKEN BLOOD? **WHAT A RIP-OFF!**

WHO HAS SUMMONED ME?
THE EASTER BUNNY.
AND WHAT KNOWLEDGE DO YOU SEEK?
I DON'T WANT TO BE THE EASTER BUNNY ANYMORE.

YOU INSULT ME WITH YOUR INSIGNIFICANT QUESTION! OF WHAT IMPORT TO A SHADOW IS A TRIVIAL HOLIDAY?

TRIVIAL HOLIDAY? YOU'RE THE SHADOW OF A GROUNDHOG! YOU DO THAT **"GROUND HOG'S DAY"** THING!
ONLY ONCE A YEAR. THE REST OF THE TIME I'M ALL IMPRESSIVE AND STUFF!

THE LIGHT DESTROYED THE SHADOW! IT'S GONE!

WHOA, RIFF'S NEW AMBIENT HALOGEN FLASH-LIGHT ACTUALLY WORKS! I MEAN BESIDES IT GIVING ME AN ICE-CREAM HEADACHE!

IT'S THE UNDERWEAR THAT MAKES IT SQUISHY! ... WHAT? ... YES, I WAS CHANGING THE SUBJECT. ...I'M ON IT. OVER AND OUT.

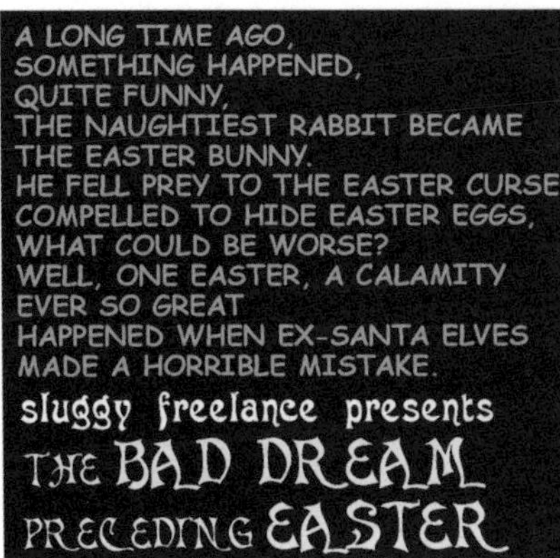

A LONG TIME AGO,
SOMETHING HAPPENED,
QUITE FUNNY,
THE NAUGHTIEST RABBIT BECAME
THE EASTER BUNNY.
HE FELL PREY TO THE EASTER CURSE.
COMPELLED TO HIDE EASTER EGGS,
WHAT COULD BE WORSE?
WELL, ONE EASTER, A CALAMITY
EVER SO GREAT
HAPPENED WHEN EX-SANTA ELVES
MADE A HORRIBLE MISTAKE.
sluggy freelance presents
THE BAD DREAM
PRECEDING EASTER

This time, this time
Making Easter
Making Easter*
EGGS
*SUNG TO THE TUNE OF "MAKING CHRISTMAS" (FROM "THE NIGHTMARE BEFORE CHRISTMAS") BY DANNY ELFMAN

Making Easter,
making Easter
Is so fine
It's hours of time
And all these eggs
must all be dyed
It's hours of our time
EGGS

Time to feed kids something fun
They'll rot their teeth
for years to come
Let's sneak ourselves
a chocolate bun
Hey it's hollow!

Making Easter,
making Easter
This elf device
paints the eggs
so nice
Like candy canes
and pretty snow
It's hours of
our time

All together,
eggs,
filled creams
With jellybeans
we're Making
Eastertime
BUN-BUN'S HERE!

I don't believe what's
happening to me....
The sugar rush
has me giddyyyyyy
(Or was it the booze?)
Hee, hee, hee, hee

Won't they
be impressed,
I am a genius
See how I use
"Marshmallow-
mix"
To make these
most delightful
chicks

Huh! No, no, no,
now that's all wrong
This thing will need
to be less Sasquatch
It must look good
in a thong
Try something fresher,
something Baywatch!
GET RIGHT ON IT! I'LL HURT YOU!

All together,
eggs,
filled creams
With jellybeans
we're Making
Eastertime
ECONO PACK JELLY BEANS

This time, this time
It's taking hours!!!!
Making Easter, making Easter
Bla, bla, bla
Poing

It's almost here
And we're just beat
So watch the ferret
celebrate

For when it's time
for eggs to hide
We'll all sing out...

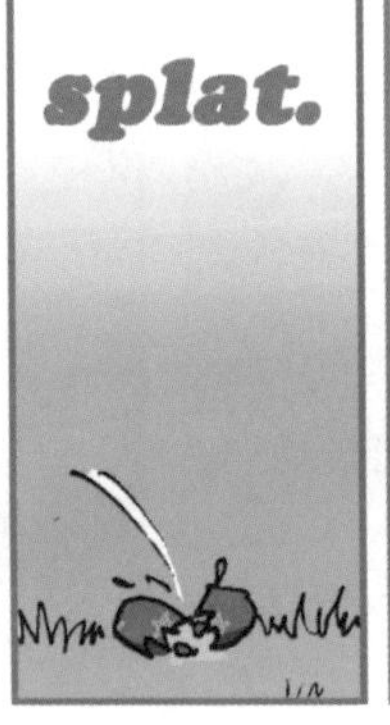

THESE EGGS WERE ALL SUPPOSED TO BE HARD-BOILED.
GOSH DARN IT ALL TO HECK!

THERE WASN'T MUCH TIME,
BUN-BUN HID EVERY ONE.
MOSTLY OUTSIDE
WHERE THEY SAT IN THE SUN.
SO ALL OF THE KIDS
WHO WENT EASTER EGG SPOTTIN'
HAD TO CHECK THAT THE EGGS
WEREN'T RAW OR GONE-ROTTEN.
OH SURE, THAT EASTER
THEY RISKED SALMONELLA,
BUT I'M STILL RATHER FOND
OF THAT BUN-BUN FELLA.
I ASKED "IF YOU COULD DO IT
ALL OVER, WHAT WOULD YOU DO?"
HE TURNED...
AND ASKED SOFTLY OF ME...
"HAND OVER YOUR CASH
OR I'LL KILL YOU."
fin

IT FINALLY FEELS LIKE SPRING! I DON'T THINK ANYTHING CAN RUIN MY GOOD MOOD.

SPRING! SPRING! SPRING!
SPRING! SPRING! SPRING!

"OH", GOD SAYS, "A CHALLENGE!"

OH, BOY! OH, BOY!

MAN-O -MAN!
POING POING POING!

HOT-DOG!

WHAT'S GOT YOU ALL EXCITED?
HOTDOG.

BOO!

I WAS HIDING BEHIND THAT TREE!
I KNEW YOU WERE THERE.

BUN-BUN, WHY DO YOU CLEAN YOURSELF ALL THE TIME?
BECAUSE I FEEL LIKE IT.

I NEVER CLEAN MYSELF EVER!
SEE PANEL 2.

THAT'S ONE GUESS.

NOT A GUESS. I'M EXPERIMENTING WITH PSYCHOTROPIC DRUGS THAT MAKE PEOPLE CONTENT WITH EVEN THE MOST TORTUROUS SITUATIONS. I SNUCK SOME INTO BUN-BUN'S BOLOGNA SANDWICHES.

BOLOGNA SANDWICHES? BUN-BUN EATS ***CUCUMBER*** SANDWICHES!

I ATE THE BOLOGNA SANDWICHES! I **LOVE** BOLOGNA! IT'S THE GREATEST UNSOLVED SANDWICH MYSTERY ***EVER!***

SLUGGY FREELANCE
sluggy freelance

I DON'T LIKE THE IDEA OF YOU PUTTING PSYCHOTROPIC DRUGS IN OUR FOOD, RIFF. WE'RE NOT YOUR GUINEA PIGS!
THIS ISN'T ABOUT MY EXPERIMENTS, ZOË! THINK OF THE BETTER WORLD WE'D HAVE IF, EVEN FOR A SHORT TIME, WE HAD A HAPPY AND DOCILE BUN-BUN?

WHY NOT JUST GET HIM DRUNK ON RUM? IT'S WORKED BEFORE!
WHERE'S THE SCIENCE IN THAT?
HEY, RIFF! BUN-BUN LOOKS LIKE HE'S ABOUT TO CHOP KIKI INTO BITS!
NORMALLY I'D BE DISTURBED BY THIS, BUT THANKS TO THE HAPPY-JUICE YOU SNUCK IN MY SANDWICH, I'M JUST OVERJOYED ABOUT IT!

OK, "OPERATION: BOLOGNA-SANDWICH" DIDN'T WORK. PLAN-B INVOLVES THIS DART-GUN LOADED WITH HAPPY-JUICE!

pht-t
phip

QUICK, ZOË, FORCE FEED THIS "PB&J" TO THE RABBIT, STAT!

LET'S GO, TORG.
I THOUGHT IT WAS FUNNY! I LOOOOVE YOUR JOKES!

FIRST GOOD MOOD I'VE BEEN IN IN A LONG TIME AND YOU'VE RUINED IT! IT'S BUTT-KICKING TIME!
HELP!

WANT A PEANUT BUTTER AND JELLY SANDWICH?
NO THANKS! TRYING TO CUT DOWN.

HEEEEEELP!
pht-t
phip

SO, ANYWAYS...

SMACK
HACK
WRAP
WAP
CHAP
TAP
GAP
CRACK
BAP
SLAP
MAP
LAP

JOY!

I SUPPOSE MY MISCALCULATION WAS IN FOCUSING MORE ON THE "HAPPY" AND NOT ENOUGH ON THE "DOCILE".
I LOVE LACERATIONS!

"TRIASSIC, JURASSIC, CRETACEOUS; PERIODS OF THE MESOZOIC ERA. SCIENCE HAS ANSWERED MANY QUESTIONS ABOUT OUR PAST, BUT ONE QUESTION HAS BAFFLED PALEONTOLOGISTS FOR AGES:"

RELAX, FOLKS, IT'S THE HEAD OF A PLUSH CARIBOU. WE THINK.

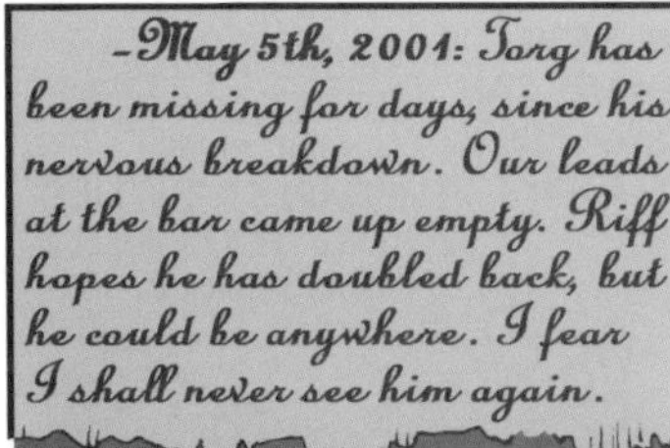
–May 5th, 2001: Torg has been missing for days, since his nervous breakdown. Our leads at the bar came up empty. Riff hopes he has doubled back, but he could be anywhere. I fear I shall never see him again.

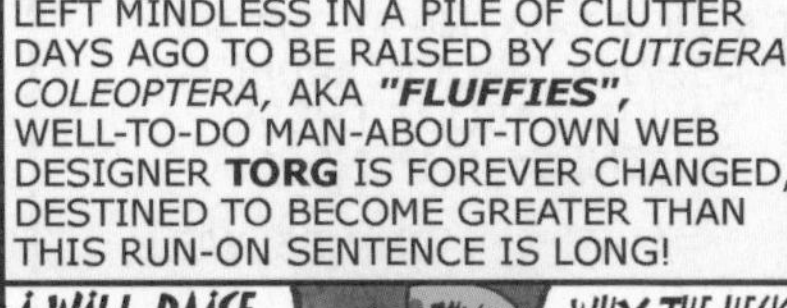
LEFT MINDLESS IN A PILE OF CLUTTER DAYS AGO TO BE RAISED BY *SCUTIGERA COLEOPTERA*, AKA ***"FLUFFIES"***, WELL-TO-DO MAN-ABOUT-TOWN WEB DESIGNER **TORG** IS FOREVER CHANGED, DESTINED TO BECOME GREATER THAN THIS RUN-ON SENTENCE IS LONG!

I WILL RAISE HIM AS MY OWN CHILD.
WHY THE HECK ARE WE CALLED "FLUFFIES"?
CAN'T WE JUST FEED ON INSECTS OR OTHER SMALL ARTHROPODS LIKE EVERYBODY ELSE?
I DON'T KNOW. I MUST HAVE BEEN OUT FOR THAT MEETING.

NOW, HE IS REMEMBERED IN LEGEND AS
Torgo of the Fluffies
KING OF THE CLUTTER!
WHO IS THIS GUY? HE'S ONLY GOT TWO FEET!
KEEP YOUR VOICE DOWN! HAVE YOU SEEN THE SIZE OF THOSE THINGS?
OO-OOO! CHITTER-CHITTER! EEEE!

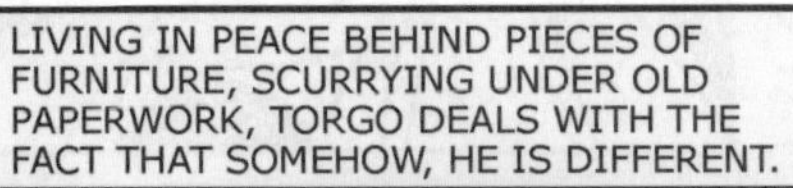
LIVING IN PEACE BEHIND PIECES OF FURNITURE, SCURRYING UNDER OLD PAPERWORK, TORGO DEALS WITH THE FACT THAT SOMEHOW, HE IS DIFFERENT.

PA? WHY DON'T I HAVE POISON GLANDS AND TWO PAIRS OF MAXILLAE?
'CAUSE YOU'RE A FREAK. NOW PUT COMEDY CENTRAL ON, IT'S TIME FOR THE DAILY SHOW.

WHEN POACHERS ENTER THE CLUTTER, IT IS UP TO TORGO TO PROTECT HIS FLUFFY BRETHREN.

BOOT
FOUND TORG.

WHEN ZOË ARRIVES, TORGO FINDS THAT WHAT HE LACKS IN BODY-SEGMENTS, HE MAKES UP IN HEART.

Oh, Torgo of the Clutter, I am *so* happy to be your fluffy Zoë!
OH, GOOD GOD!
DO WE *HAVE* TO BE PART OF THIS DREAM?

LOST IN HIS VISION, TORGO IS CAUGHT OFF GUARD AS THE FLYER FOR RED LOBSTER HE IS HIDING UNDER IS FLIPPED OVER.
TORG?
eep!

IN A PANIC MOVE, TAUGHT TO HIM FROM **DAYS** OF LIVING WITH THE FLUFFIES, TORGO STREAKS ACROSS THE ROOM WITH LIGHTNING SPEED TO HIDE BEHIND THE HEAVY METAL FILING CABINET.
ZIP!

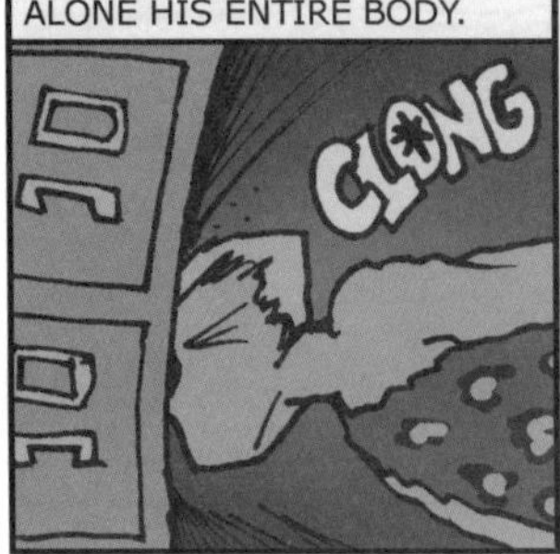
UNFORTUNATELY, THE SPACE BETWEEN THE WALL AND THE CABINET IS NOT ENOUGH FOR TORGO'S CRANIUM, LET ALONE HIS ENTIRE BODY.
CLONG

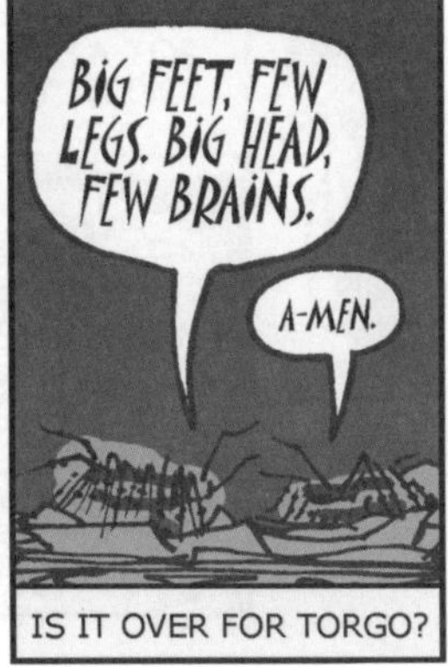
BIG FEET, FEW LEGS. BIG HEAD, FEW BRAINS.
A-MEN.
IS IT OVER FOR TORGO?

TORG?
ZOË? I...

EEEEEYYYYOOO! GET THEM OFF ME!
OW!
HEY!
QUIT IT!
I'LL JUST WAIT FOR YOU ***WAY OUT HERE!***
THAT'S GRATITUDE FOR YA!
Sluggy Freelance

AYLEE? WHY AM I THOUSANDS OF DOLLARS IN DEBT?
TORG, I'M THE SECRETARY FOR YOUR WEB DESIGN BUSINESS. YOU RUNNING UP A FEW GRAND IN CREDIT CARD DEBT FROM THERAPIST BILLS IS NOT MY DEPARTMENT.
TAK TAK TAK

I'M NOT TALKING ABOUT MY *PERSONAL* CREDIT CARD! I'M TALKING ABOUT **THESE BUSINESS EXPENSES!**

OH! YES. WELL, I DIDN'T WANT TO UPSET YOU.

A FEW GRAND IN THERAPIST BILLS?
THERE YOU GO, GETTING UPSET AGAIN. MY THERAPIST THINKS YOU'RE TOO EASILY EXCITABLE.

WELL, BETWEEN BUSINESS EXPENSES AND AYLEE'S THERAPIST COSTS, I AM IN THE RED, DEEP. THERE'S NO WAY OUT OF THIS ONE. I'M OVER. FINISHED. TOAST.
IF YOU'RE IN TOO MUCH DEBT, WHY DON'T YOU FILE FOR BANKRUPTCY?

BANKRUPTCY! WHY DIDN'T I THINK OF THAT! THANKS, RIFF! THAT SOLVES **EVERYTHING!**
WELL, IF YOU CAN PULL IT OFF, IT GETS RID OF YOUR DEBT. BUT YOU'RE STILL GOING TO NEED MONEY FOR FOOD AND RENT AND STUFF!

YOU MEAN THEY DON'T GIVE YOU LOTS OF MONEY WHEN YOU GO BANKRUPT?
I DON'T THINK SO.
THAT'S UN-AMERICAN!

SO, I HEAR TORG'S FREELANCE BUSINESS WENT UNDER.
YEAH. WONDER WHAT HE'S GOING TO DO NOW.

MAYBE GET A "REAL" JOB LIKE EVERYONE ELSE.

I'M THE ONLY ONE AT THIS TABLE WITH A REAL JOB, AREN'T I?
I'M LOOKING. YOU GOT A PROBLEM WITH THAT?
I'M A FULL-TIME STUDENT!
I'M MAKING A DEATH-RAY GUN OUT OF STRAWS AND ICE CUBES!

5 MINUTES LATER...

ONE DAY I AWOKE WASHED UP ON THE SHORE OF A STRANGE ISLAND. THE ONLY EVIDENCE OF HOW I GOT THERE WAS AN EMPTY BOTTLE OF TEQUILA AND A STRANGE RECOLLECTION OF BEING ON A THREE-HOUR TOUR.
sluggy freelance presents
a Riff story
the Isle of the Ployees

I QUICKLY FOUND THE ISLAND WAS INHABITED.
WHAT ARE YOU? WHERE AM I?
THIS IS THE ISLE OF THE **PLOYEES.** BROWNBEAK WILL WANT TO SEE YOU!

I WAS TAKEN TO THE LEADER OF THE TRIBAL "PLOYEES".
I AM **BROWNBEAK** OF THE PLOYEES. WE WELCOME YOU TO OUR HOME!

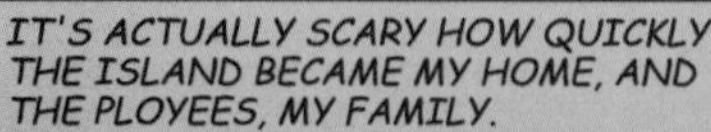
IT'S ACTUALLY SCARY HOW QUICKLY THE ISLAND BECAME MY HOME, AND THE PLOYEES, MY FAMILY.

INSTANT SCARY INITIATION RITUAL
CLAP CLAP CLAP CLAP CLAP CLAP CLAP

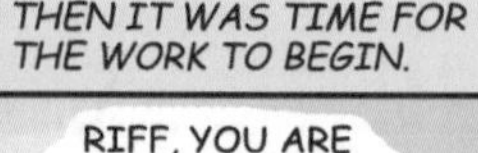
THEN IT WAS TIME FOR THE WORK TO BEGIN.

RIFF, YOU ARE INITIATED; IT IS TIME FOR YOU TO DO AS THE PLOYEES DO.

"THIS IS A MAGIC ISLAND, TEEMING WITH BEASTS WE CALL **PR'JEX.** SOARING PR'JEX, SIMPLE PR'JEX. ALL KINDS. ALL WILD."

WE TAME THEM. YOU WILL TAME THEM TOO.
WHY?

WE DO IT FOR ***EEOH, THE SEA GOD*** WHO PROTECTS US. WE TAME THE PR'JEX FOR HIM WHO FEEDS US, REWARDS US, DEFENDS US...
NOT "WHY DO WE DO IT". WHY WOULD *I* WANT TO DO IT?

OH! BECAUSE IF YOU DON'T, WE'LL THROW YOU INTO THE VOLCANO.
GOTCHA. LET'S GET A-TAMING!

AS IT TURNED OUT, KEEPING OUT OF THE VOLCANO WAS THE REAL NAME OF THE GAME THERE. SOMETIMES TWO, THREE, EVEN TEN GUYS GOT 'CANO-TOSSED A DAY.
Yaaa!

I THOUGHT IT ALL HAD TO DO WITH HOW WELL YOU DID YOUR JOB, BUT IT WAS ACTUALLY A VERY COMPLICATED ALGORITHM THAT BROWNBEAK SHARED WITH ME ONE DAY. TURNS OUT THE BEST THING I COULD DO WAS TAME THE PR'JEX AND KEEP MY HEAD DOWN. IT STILL DIDN'T GUARANTEE MY SAFETY FROM A SKINNY-DIP IN THE LAVA-POOL.
Do I like you?
You like me?
blood relative
* nepotis
if bribe < WORK ETHIC THEN
$$$
((x + WORK) - ugly) =
no tie? * softball team

SO WE SPENT OUR DAYS, EVERY DAY, TRYING TO TAME THE STRANGE AND WONDROUS CREATURES. IT WASN'T AS EASY AS IT LOOKS, SINCE THE ONLY METHOD THE PLOYEES HAD TO TAME THESE MONSTERS WAS BY WHACKING THEM IN THE FACE WITH A "TAMING STICK".
WAP WAP WAP WAP WAP WAP WAP WAP WAP WAP

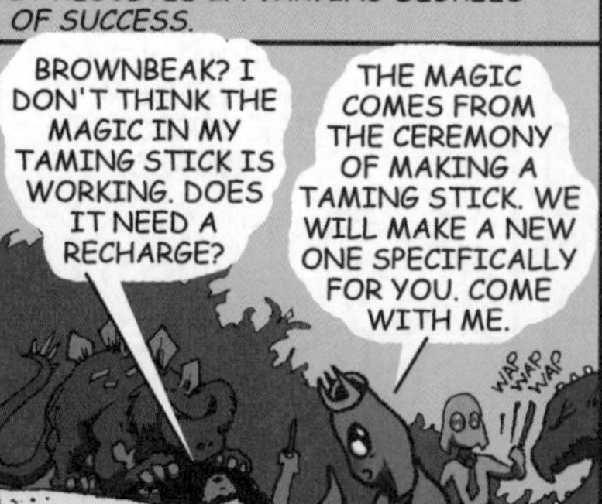
IT RESULTED IN VARYING DEGREES OF SUCCESS.
BROWNBEAK? I DON'T THINK THE MAGIC IN MY TAMING STICK IS WORKING. DOES IT NEED A RECHARGE?
THE MAGIC COMES FROM THE CEREMONY OF MAKING A TAMING STICK. WE WILL MAKE A NEW ONE SPECIFICALLY FOR YOU. COME WITH ME.
WAP WAP WAP

YOU FIND A STICK...

WAP
OW!
IT WORKS!

ONE DAY, BROWNBEAK RETURNED FROM HIS DAILY MEDITATIONS WITH EEOH, FOLLOWED (CHASED) BY THE LARGEST PR'JEK I HAD EVER SEEN!
EEOH, THE GREAT GOD OF THE SEA, HAS BLESSED US WITH THE **CATZ-TWENTY-TWO!** MIGHTIEST OF THE PR'JEX.

GREAT EVIL WILL BEFALL US IF WE FAIL TO TAME HIM BEFORE THE "LION OF THE DEAD" ARRIVES, BUT HOW CAN WE **FAIL** AN ASSIGNMENT THIS **GRAND?**
BECAUSE IT'S TOO BIG?
THOOM THOOM THOOM

*THE "**LION OF THE DEAD"** WAS A LION-LIKE PR'JEK, WHICH STRUTTED OUT OF THE SEA TO SIGNIFY THE END OF THE WORK SEASON. OF COURSE ONE BAD THING WAS THAT THE NEXT WORK SEASON BEGAN THE NEXT DAY. A WORSE THING WAS, TO MY UNDER-STANDING, IT WAS RIGHT AROUND THE CORNER.*

WE HAVE TO TAME THIS THING BEFORE THE LION OF THE DEAD, OR ELSE?
AREN'T WE **LUCKY?** WON'T THIS BE **GRAND?** I'M PUTTING YOU IN CHARGE.
THOOM THOOM THOOM
ROAR

RIFF WILL BE THE TEAM LEADER IN CHARGE OF TAMING THE ***CATZ-TWENTY-TWO!***
YEAH!
YEAH!
HEAR-HEAR!
GO, RIFF!

DIDN'T THAT TIKI-IDOL SAY GREAT EVIL WILL BEFALL US IF WE SCREW THIS UP? MIGHT WANT TO GIVE THIS TO SOMEONE WITH MORE EXPERIENCE.
YOU'LL BE ***FINE!*** YOU HAVE MY FULL SUPPORT!
FSSSSSSSSS

I WHACK HIM IN THE FACE WITH THIS STICK UNTIL HE DOES WHAT WE TELL HIM.
YUP.

AND IF I DON'T, YOU THROW ME IN THE VOLCANO.
YUP.

I'M GOING TO NEED A BIGGER STICK.
WE DON'T HAVE A BUDGET FOR THAT.

SLUGGY FREELANCE

the Isle of the Ployees

ROAR!

I KNEW THE TAMING STICK WOULD NEVER WORK ON THE CATZ-TWENTY-TWO, BUT AS YOU KNOW, I'M PRETTY RESOURCEFUL. IF I COULD CONVINCE BROWNBEAK TO LET ME UPGRADE MY TAMING STICK, EVERYONE WOULD BE BETTER OFF.

BROWNBEAK, SEE THAT SOARING PR'JEK OVER THERE?
RIFF'S TAME-O-MATIC

I JUST NEEDED TO GIVE HIM AN EXAMPLE.
TWANG!

boom!

Splatity-splatitysplat-spaltity SPLAT.

BAD EXAMPLE.
I ***LIKE*** IT!

MARK AND TING WERE TWO MINDS, FORCED BY AN ANCIENT CURSE TO SHARE THE SAME BODY BUT NEVER THE SAME IDEA. THIS MADE IT DIFFICULT TO GET THEM BOTH TO AGREE ON APPROVING MY INVENTION.

SARCASM WAS LOST ON MARK AND TING ALTHOUGH I FINALLY GOT THEM TO AGREE WITH EACH OTHER.

THROW HIM IN THE VOLCANO!

BROWNBEAK! DON'T LET THEM THROW ME INTO THE VOLCANO! YOU KNOW I'M YOUR ONLY HOPE TO TAME THE CATZ TWENTY-TWO IN TIME!
YES. YOU ARE RIGHT. YOU AND I MUST SPEAK TO THE GREAT EEOH.
DARN! HE WENT OVER OUR HEADS.

AND SO, THE GREAT EEOH OF THE SEA WAS SUMMONED.
I AM SUMMONED.
WHOA!

UM, I WANTED TO TALK ABOUT GETTING THE PLOYEES BETTER TOOLS SO WE CAN GET THE CATZ-TWENTY-TWO TAMED BY THE LION OF THE DEAD.
The synergy of our multimedian experience must be conducive to econotric growth!

SPLASH!
HUH? THAT WAS IT?
WISE ARE HIS WORDS!

THE WORDS OF THE GREAT **EEOH** WERE EMPTY. I REALIZED NOBODY WAS RUNNING THE ASYLUM. NOT **BROWNBEAK**. NOT **MARK** AND **TING**. AND NOT THE **SEA EEOH**. THERE WAS NO PURPOSE TO THE WORK THE **PLOYEES** DID. BUT I WOULD GIVE THEM A PURPOSE!

Sluggy Freelance Presents:
PLOYEES, LISTEN TO ME! THROW DOWN YOUR TAMING STICKS. I WANT OFF THIS CRAZY ISLAND, SO I'M BUILDING A BOAT. ANY WHO WANT TO COME WITH ME, LEND A HAND.
BUT WE CAN'T, RIFF! IF WE TAKE A BOAT OUT ON THIS SEA, THE TERROR FROM BEYOND THE HORIZON WILL DESTROY US!

THE SEA EEOH PROTECTS US FROM THE TERROR BEYOND THE HORIZON!
WHAT IS THIS "TERROR BEYOND THE HORIZON"?
WE DON'T KNOW.
IT'S, LIKE, ALWAYS HIDING BEYOND THE HORIZON.
IT MUST BE REALLY SCARY!
THAT TERROR IS THE GREAT EVIL THAT WILL BEFALL US IF WE DON'T TAME THE CATZ TWENTY-TWO BY THE DEAD LION.

NONE OF THE PLOYEES WANTED TO HELP ME WITH THE BOAT, SO I DECIDED TO GET A TAN INSTEAD. EVENTUALLY, THE DAY CAME, AND THE LION OF THE DEAD ROSE FROM THE SEA. THE SEA EEOH ARRIVED WITH HIS HEAD BOWED. AND WITHOUT MY HELP, THE CATZ-TWENTY- TWO WAS STILL WILD AS EVER.

The Isle of the Ployees
I'M HERE! END OF THE WORK SEASON! WHERE'S THE PARTY?
MAY OUR DEATHS COME SWIFT. MAY OUR DEATHS COME SWIFT. MAY OUR DEATHS COME SWIFT.
Our supply chain management lies at the heart of our disconnect.
ROAR!

GET OFF YOUR KNEES! NOTHING HAS HAPPENED! I TOLD YOU, THE ONLY THING BEYOND THE HORIZON IS FREEDOM! NOW, LET'S GET WORKING ON A BOAT!

THE TERROR FROM BEYOND THE HORIZON! IT COMES!
UH-OH.
YOU GUYS ARE SCREWED. I AM OUT OF HERE.

I AM INVESTOR, AND YOU HAVE ALL ANGERED ME!

WITH UNBELIEVABLE POWER AND SPEED HE DESTROYED THE SEA EEOH AND TURNED THE CATZ-TWENTY-TWO TO DUST.

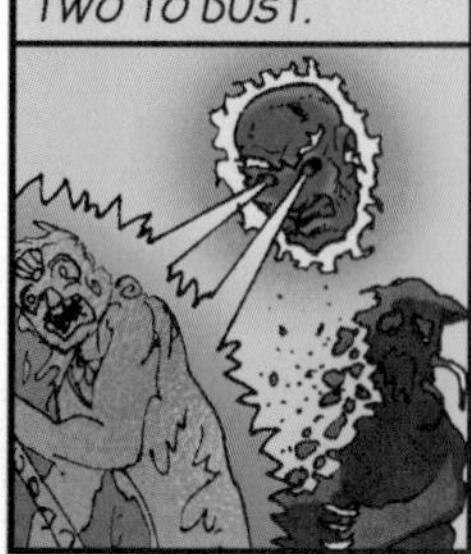

A NEW SEA EEOH APPEARED, MEANER AND MORE CRYPTIC.

OUR MISSION STATEMENT IS TO DIVERSIFY OUR NETWORK FABRIC TO INCREASE OUTPUT A THOUSAND-FOLD! ***MUAHA-HAHAHAHA!***

BUT WORSE TORMENT BEFELL THE POOR, POOR PLOYEES.

HE DOWNSIZED US, YOU BIG DUMB JERK!

AND THEY THREW ME INTO THE VOLCANO.

LUCKILY THE VOLCANO WAS ACTUALLY A MAGIC PORTAL THAT RETURNED ME TO THE REAL WORLD. IT WAS MY SALVATION, NOT MY DESTRUCTION. I LEARNED AN IMPORTANT LESSON THAT DAY. LAVA HEALS ALL WOUNDS. WHEN LIFE GETS ME DOWN, I LOOK TO JUMP IN SOME LAVA. BARRING THAT, I REMEMBER THAT FREEDOM IS NOT FOUND ON THE HORIZON. TRUE FREEDOM IS FOUND BY LOOKING WITHIN. WITHIN MOUNTAINS FILLED WITH LAVA.

FIN

OH, I GET IT. MARK AND TING ARE "MARKETING". SEA EEOH IS THE "C.E.O.". YOU MADE UP A FAIRY TALE TO SHOW ME HOW MESSED UP THE CORPORATE WORLD IS.
NO, ACTUALLY IT'S THE DREAM I HAD LAST NIGHT. COOL HUH?

I THOUGHT YOU SAID IT WOULD SHATTER MY CONFIDENCE ABOUT THIS JOB!
YEAH. NOW YOU'RE TWO HOURS LATE FOR YOUR INTERVIEW.

DREAM, HUH? YOU KNOW WHAT FREUD WOULD SAY ABOUT YOU BEING THROWN IN A VOLCANO, RIGHT?
TORG, SOMETIMES A CIGAR IS A CIGAR, AND A PINK SLIP IS LADIES UNDERWEAR.

DO YOU THINK YOUR NEW GRILL WILL BE READY FOR MEMORIAL DAY?
IT CAN ALREADY COOK A T-BONE WELL DONE IN 2.539 SECONDS!

WOW, THAT'S A LOT OF POWER!
THIS GRILL WOULD SHOOT A PILLAR OF FIRE A HUNDRED FEET INTO THE AIR IF I DIDN'T INSTALL THIS HANDY-DANDY VENTING PIPE!

fooosh!

WHAT IF I WANT MY STEAK RARE?
I'M WORKING ON A 50-FOOT TALL GRILL-RACK ATTACHMENT.

THANKS FOR LETTING ME BORROW SOME CLOTHES, GWYNN! IF I WEREN'T LATE FOR FINALS ALREADY I'D BE WOUNDING RIFF FOR BARBECUING MY CLEAN LAUNDRY.
THE REAL TRAGEDY IS THAT I'M GOING TO HAVE TO WAIT UNTIL YOU GET HOME TO FIND OUT WHAT THAT LAST THING YOU SAID MEANT.
ZOË

ODD. I WOULD HAVE THOUGHT THAT ZOE'D PICK AN OUTFIT THAT COVERED THAT TATTOO ON HER CHEST. THOUGHT SHE WAS EMBARRASSED BY IT.

I'M GOING TO KILL GWYNN! NO, WAIT. I WAS THE ONE WHO PICKED THIS OUTFIT. CAN'T KILL MYSELF... I KNOW! I'LL KILL RIFF! I CAN ALWAYS KILL RIFF!

HOW'D YOUR FINALS GO?

WHO COULD CONCENTRATE ON FINALS WHEN I'VE GOT THIS TO LOOK AT? IT WAS ALL "LOOK! ZOË'S GOT A TATTOO!", "DID IT HURT, ZOË?", "CAN I TOUCH IT, ZOË?", "IT'S SO COOL, ZOË!"...

AND I GOT ASKED OUT SEVEN TIMES IN AN HOUR! THAT'S MORE TIMES THAN IN MY WHOLE COLLEGE CAREER!
DID YOU SAY YES TO ANY OF THEM?
SURE, GWYNN! I COULDN'T WAIT TO GO OUT WITH SOME FRAT-BOY WHO ASSUMED I WAS EASY BECAUSE I HAD A TATTOO!

WELL, I'M SORRY YOU HAD SUCH A BAD DAY.
IT RULED!

HI TORG!
HI, AYLEE! I WAS JUST CHECKING THE NEWSPAPER AND I THINK I FOUND ONE JOB THAT LOOKS TEMPTING!

SINCE IT'S UNDER MY OWN ROOF THE COMMUTE WOULD BE A SNAP!
OH! THAT. I NEED TO HIRE SOME HELP. SINCE YOUR WEB DESIGN BUSINESS WENT UNDER, I DECIDED TO TRY RUNNING ONE MYSELF.

YEAH. ON MY CREDIT CARDS. AYLEE, IF YOU WANTED TO DO SOMETHING LIKE THAT, WHY DIDN'T YOU JUST COME TO ME?
BUT...BUT...
MOVE IT!
OH, YOU'RE HERE FOR THIS JOB? GIVE ME YOUR RESUME AND GO WAIT OVER THERE WITH THE OTHERS.

GWYNN?
WHAT? I NEED A JOB!

HOW'S AYLEE'S FREELANCE WEB DESIGN GOING?
SO FAR, SO GOOD.

KIND OF IRONIC, HUH? YOU SWITCHED PLACES AND NOW YOU'RE HER SECRETARY.
WHAT? I HAVE YEARS OF SOLID WEB DESIGN EXPERIENCE, WHY WOULD I SETTLE FOR THAT JOB? BESIDES, GWYNN'S THE SECRETARY NOW.
AY:LEE!
THAT'S ADMINISTRATIVE ASSISTANT.

SO, WEB-GUY, WHY IS YOUR "OFFICE" A CLOSET WITH ONE PHONE AND NO COMPUTER?

YOU'RE THE RECEPTIONIST!
THAT'S CHIEF COMMUNICATIONS OFFICER.

LOOKING GOOD, ZOË! THAT'S A NEW LOOK FOR YOU, ISN'T IT?
FIGURED I'D TRY IT SINCE RIFF BARBECUED ALL MY OLD CLOTHES.
I'VE FOUND THAT MEN WILL BARBECUE ANYTHING.
FIRST AID
SLUGGY FREELANCE

THIS SUCKS!
I CAN'T BELIEVE WE'RE STUCK HERE WORKING ON MEMORIAL DAY, FOR CRYING OUT LOUD!

"WORKING?" IS THAT WHAT YOU CALL IT? LOOKS TO ME LIKE YOU'RE BOTH STARING OUT A WINDOW WHEN YOU SHOULD BE WORKING!

I'M ON BREAK.
THIS IS A JOKE! YOU'VE HIRED ME AS A RECEPTIONIST FOR A WEB BUSINESS WHERE YOU'VE DONE EVERYTHING THROUGH THE INTERNET! NO ONE HAS CALLED YET! AND MY OFFICE IS A CLOSET!

I CAN'T HELP BUT THINK, "I KNEW IT," EVERY TIME YOU COME OUT OF THE CLOSET, TORG.
AND THAT'S THE ONLY JOKE GWYNN KNOWS SO I HAVE TO HEAR IT FIFTEEN TIMES A DAY!

ALL YOU DO IS COMPLAIN, TORG. AND I FINALLY FIGURED OUT WHY. YOU'RE JEALOUS!
JEALOUS?!?

JEALOUS OF MY SUCCESS AT A HOME BUSINESS!
YOU MUST BE RIGHT. IT'S NOT THAT I'M WORKING HARD AT DOING NOTHING IN A CLOSET ON A NATIONAL HOLIDAY! WHAT IS THIS, SOME OLD TV SITCOM?
WELL, I HAVE BEEN WATCHING MORE "NICK AT NIGHT" LATELY...

DON'T CHANGE THE SUBJECT, TORG. AND DON'T GET ALL SMART-ALECKY WITH ME! IF YOU DON'T THINK YOU CAN HANDLE THE JOB, I'LL JUST GET SOMEBODY ELSE!
SHUT UP, BOTH OF YOU. I ALMOST WISH THIS WERE AN OLD TV SITCOM. AT LEAST THEN THIS WHOLE THING WOULD BE RESOLVED BY THE END OF THE EPISODE.

SHE'S RIGHT, TORG.
I LOVE YOU GUYS!

The End

HAPPY MEMORIAL DAY!
CLINK
I'M STILL ON BREAK!
GRRR
RIFF? I WANTED MY BURGER RARE.
IT'S THE ONLY ONE OF ITS KIND.
POTATO SALADE
OOPS!
THUNK
WATCH IT, TUBE-RAT.
FOOOSH!

WITH OUR NEW CLIENT INFLUX, OUR PROJECTED EARNINGS LOOK GREAT. SINCE OUR ACTUAL EARNINGS ARE ICKY, I'M GOING TO HAVE TO LET YOU GO.
TORG, I'M SORRY.

YOU'RE FIRING ME?
WE DON'T NEED A RECEPTIONIST. NOBODY CALLS US ANYWAY. WE'RE ONLINE MOSTLY.

GWYNN WRAPPED A TREE AROUND YOU AND TRIED TO SQUEEZE YOU TO DEATH!
NO FAIR! I WAS POSSESSED!
AND YOU'RE KEEPING SPUDDY-BUDDY ON THE PAYROLL?
HE'S "PLUSH UNION". I HAVE NO CHOICE.

WELL?

WHERE AM I GOING TO GO? THIS IS MY APARTMENT!
COULD YOU TAKE OFF THE TIE? IT'S CONFUSING.

GWYNN? I'M SO HAPPY YOU'RE WORKING OUT SO WELL AS MY SECRETARY. BACK WHEN I WAS TORG'S SECRETARY, HE GAVE ME A GIFT, AND NOW IT IS ONLY FITTING TO SHARE IT WITH YOU.

EEEEK!
WHAT ARE YOU DOING?

THERE WILL BE NO SQUISHING OF MY PET FLUFFY WHILE YOU ARE WORKING FOR ME! IN FACT, I'M MAKING IT PART OF YOUR JOB RESPONSIBILITIES TO TAKE CARE OF HIM!

BOSSES SUCK, HUH?
I HATE BUGS.

HEY, TORG. YOU SEEM TO BE IN A BETTER MOOD!
AYLEE'S BUSINESS IS STARTING TO REALLY TAKE OFF! SHE'S GOT A GREAT HANDLE ON WEB DESIGN.

BUT ONE CONCEPT SHE NEVER REALLY FULLY GRASPED WAS ACCOUNTING. MONEY. WHERE IT COMES FROM, (USUALLY MY CREDIT CARDS) OR WHERE IT GOES (LIKE THAT THERAPIST SHE'S SEEING). ALL THE MONEY TO FUND AYLEE'S BUSINESS COMES OUT OF MY POCKET.
GUESS WHERE ALL THE PROFIT IS GOING?

HEY! YOU GOT A NEW PS2!
AND A BANK STATEMENT.

SO YOU'RE MAKING AS MUCH MONEY AS RUNNING YOUR OWN BUSINESS WITHOUT ANY WORK.
IF YOU THINK GETTING THROUGH "RED FACTION" IN HARD-MODE ISN'T WORK, YOU'VE GOT ANOTHER THING COMING!
BUDDA BUDDA BUDDA
KA-BOOM!

STILL PLAYING "RED FACTION", RIFF?
THIS RULES! YOU CAN BLOW UP ALMOST EVERYTHING IN THE GAME!
THAT LAST ROOM LOOKS LIKE SWISS CHEESE!
RIFF, YOU ALREADY BLOW UP "ALMOST EVERYTHING"! ISN'T THIS OVERKILL?

OHHHHH! THIS IS THAT OLD "TOO MUCH OF A GOOD THING" MYTH.
I THOUGHT THAT WAS JUST AN URBAN LEGEND. QUICK, BLOW UP THAT SHINY THING!
OOOH!

TORG!
BERT! HOLY COW! HOW HAVE YOU BEEN?

I HAD TO WARN YOU BEFORE IT'S TOO LATE! I HAD THIS HORRIBLE VISION OF YOU FLEEING FOR YOUR LIFE WHILE FLYING BY THE CROTCH PLANET IN A GIANT SPACE-CROTCH.

EVERYTHING'S "CROTCH" WITH YOU, ISN'T IT, BERT?
YOU HAVE NO IDEA!

SPEAKING OF WHICH, HOW'S THE BABOON CROTCH-TRANSPLANT WORKING OUT?
ITCHY AND...
QUESTION WITHDRAWN.

SORRY TO HEAR ABOUT YOU DOING SO BAD AT FINALS, ZOË.

HOW DID YOU FIND OUT? I DIDN'T TELL ANYONE!
ONE OF YOUR PROFESSORS LEFT A FUNERARY WREATH ON YOUR DOORSTEP.
Sluggy Freelance

"IN MEMORY OF YOUR 2.0." GOT TO LOVE A FACULTY WITH A SENSE OF HUMOR.

I'VE GOTTEN GREAT CONTROL OVER MY NEW FORM THESE DAYS. I HARDLY EVER ACCIDENTALLY RELEASE AN ELECTRO-MAGNETIC PULSE ANYMORE. BUT NOW GWYNN AND TORG HATE ME, WHEN I'M ONLY TRYING TO HELP. GWYNN WAS EVEN GOING TO SQUISH "FLUFFY", MY PET. AND TORG SEEMED TO BE ON HER SIDE!
Dr. Bláoun
Alien Therapist
PhD., Md., Et.

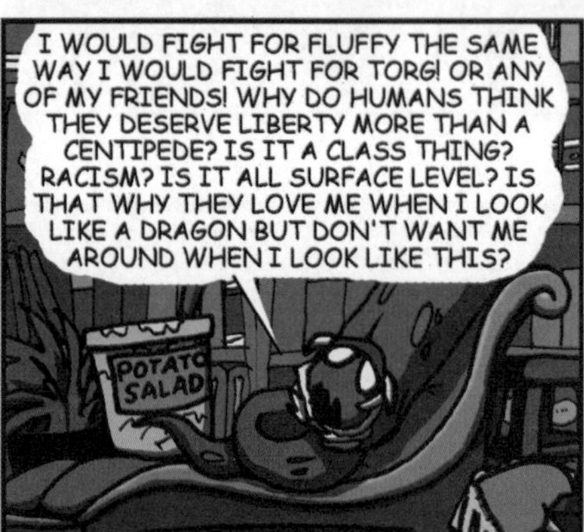
I WOULD FIGHT FOR FLUFFY THE SAME WAY I WOULD FIGHT FOR TORG! OR ANY OF MY FRIENDS! WHY DO HUMANS THINK THEY DESERVE LIBERTY MORE THAN A CENTIPEDE? IS IT A CLASS THING? RACISM? IS IT ALL SURFACE LEVEL? IS THAT WHY THEY LOVE ME WHEN I LOOK LIKE A DRAGON BUT DON'T WANT ME AROUND WHEN I LOOK LIKE THIS?
POTATO SALAD

YOU HAVE A LOT MORE QUESTIONS THAN USUAL FOR ME, AYLEE.
THERE ARE SO MANY THINGS ABOUT THIS LIFE I JUST DON'T UNDERSTAND.
PERHAPS IF I TRY TO DRAW SOME CONCLUSIONS, IT WILL HELP YOU UNDERSTAND YOURSELF BETTER. AYLEE, WHAT ARE YOUR EARLIEST MEMORIES?
POTATO SALAD

ATTACKING AND EATING HUMANS ON A SPACE SHIP.
WHY DID YOU DO THAT?
BECAUSE, UM, BECAUSE IT'S WHAT I WAS SUPPOSED TO DO.
AND DID YOU EAT ALL THE HUMANS?
ALL BUT TORG AND RIFF.
ALMOST PERFECT.
POTATO SALAD

ONCE YOU GOT TO EARTH YOU GOT A JOB AS TORG'S SECRETARY. WERE YOU POLITE, CONGENIAL, AND EFFICIENT?
I MADE A FEW MISTAKES.
BUT STILL, AN ALMOST PERFECT SECRETARY.

AYLEE, SIMPLY PUT, YOU'RE A PERFECTIONIST. AND NOW YOUR FRIENDS ARE HAVING TROUBLE DEALING WITH YOUR ATTEMPTS TO BE THE PERFECT BOSS.
THEY'RE NOT THE ONLY ONES UNHAPPY! I'M UNHAPPY TOO! I'VE NEVER BEEN SO UNHAPPY!

YOUR SPECIES ADAPTS TO ITS ENVIRONMENT. WITH IT COMES AN INSTINCTIVE GOAL THAT YOU TRY TO ACHIEVE WITH NEAR PERFECT RESULTS. SO WHY DID YOUR GOALS CHANGE FROM BEING A SECRETARY TO A BOSS OF A FREELANCE WEB BUSINESS?
TO UM... HELP TORG.

YES. YOU DID IT FOR TORG, NOT SOME INSTINCTIVE MANDATE. YOU HAVE LEFT THE COMFORTABLE BIRDCAGE OF IN-STINCT TO TRY AND FLY ON YOUR OWN. YOU ARE CHARTING YOUR OWN COURSE NOW. IT IS ONLY NATURAL TO BE ANXIOUS!

IT ALL MAKES SENSE!
WORN

SORRY ABOUT THE ELECTROMAGNETIC PULSE.
NO SKIN OFF MY NOSE!

THANK YOU, DR. BLÁOUN! I FEEL A LOT BETTER.
SEE YOU NEXT WEEK, AND REMEMBER THERE IS NOTHING WRONG WITH BEING ALMOST PERFECT!

AND AS SOON AS I GET MY DATA TO RECONCILE, THERE IS NOTHING WRONG WITH MY CLONING AN ALMOST PERFECT WEAPON.
SPECIMEN 318

MY SCHOLARSHIP'S RUN OUT! I CAN'T AFFORD ANOTHER TUITION BILL. I'M SO CLOSE TO GRADUATING NOW, BUT MY PARENTS WON'T GIVE ME THE MONEY TO "WASTE" OUT HERE! WHAT AM I GONNA DO?
WHAT ABOUT THE STRIP-CLUB? YOU COULD MAKE GOOD MONEY QUICK WORKING THERE.

THAT'S NOT EXACTLY MY SCENE, GWYNN.
YEAH, BUT WHAT IF YOUR *MOM* THOUGHT IT *WAS*?

"BUT, MOM, LOTS OF WOMEN AROUND HERE DO PROFESSIONAL STRIPPING TO PAY FOR COLLEGE."
SAY "LAP-DANCING" INSTEAD OF "STRIPPING" AND THE CHECK WILL BE IN THE MAIL.

HI, MOM? IT'S ZOË.
...
CALM DOWN, MOM! NOTHING'S WRONG! I'M NOT IN THE HOSPITAL.

NO MOM, I'M NOT AT SOME "RABE" TRIPPING ON "ETCETERA"! **NO, MOM, I AM NOT STRIPPING AT CLUBS FOR EXTRA MONEY!**

LISTEN TO ME! THE REASON I CALLED IS...

do'h!

I JUST... UM... CALLED TO WISH DAD A HAPPY FATHER'S DAY EARLY.

AHA!
WHAT DO YOU MEAN "I NEVER REMEMBER FATHER'S DAY"? I'M NOT ON MIND-EXPANDING DRUGS, MOM! **IT'S CALLED A CALENDAR!**

WHY WON'T THIS DATA RECONCILE?
I'M NO EXPERT ON THAT DNA STUFF YOU APPEAR TO BE WORKING ON, BUT PERHAPS I CAN HELP, "DR. BLÁOUN!"
OH... um...uh... HI... uh...

WHEN I FIRST HEARD ABOUT AYLEE'S "ALIEN THERAPIST", I WAS CURIOUS. AS SOON AS I HEARD THE NAME "BLÁOUN", I INSTANTLY THOUGHT "BALLOON", WHICH REMINDED ME OF AN INFLATABLE TECHNOLOGY SCIENTIST. AND THEN I WONDERED, "WHAT ON EARTH WOULD HE WANT WITH AYLEE?"
CLICK!

I WANT TO HELP HER, RIFF! I *AM* AN ALIEN THERAPIST! IT'S MY NEW CALLING! IN FACT, YOU HAVE TO LEAVE. I'M FIVE MINUTES AWAY FROM MY APPOINTMENT WITH A SPACEMAN NAMED ***"LÍ ZURECAIN NON"***.

YOU MEAN, "**LASER CANNON**"?
OH, VERY FUNNY! I'M STILL GOING TO HAVE TO CHARGE YOU FOR A FULL SESSION.

IF YOU THINK I'M GOING TO LET YOU CLONE THAT ALIEN, YOU'VE GOT ANOTHER THING COMING, SCHLOCK.
WHAT YOU'VE FAILED TO REALIZE IS YOU ARE ALREADY TOO LATE. SICK HIM, AYLEE 2!

Roar!

POP!

STRAIGHT-PINS VS. INFLATABLE TECHNOLOGY; THE STRAIGHT-PIN ALWAYS WINS.
FSSSSSSSS
DARN.

HI, AYLEE! THIS IS DR. BLA'OUN!
HI DOCTOR! WHAT IS IT?
I'VE BEEN GOING OVER OUR LAST WEEK'S SESSION, AND I HAVE AMAZINGLY GOOD NEWS FOR YOU! YOU'RE 100% CURED!

IN FACT I'M EVEN GOING TO REFUND 25%... URK.. HALF... URK (come on man!).. A LOT OF YOUR FEES, JUST AS A THANK YOU FOR BRIGHTENING MY LIFE SO MUCH WITH YOUR PRESENCE!
AW, SHUCKS DOC!
I'M SURE WE'LL SEE EACH OTHER AGAIN SOON ...URK...NEVER... ACK...I MEAN I'LL KEEP YOU IN MY THOUGHTS!
ARE YOU OK, DOCTOR?

YES, I'M FINE. UM... "I'M JUST LATE FOR MY SECOND JOB. A LOT OF SCIENTISTS HERE DO PROFESSIONAL STRIPPING TO PAY FOR EVIL."
OOOH-KAY. BYE.
BYE-BYE.

WHAT A WEIRDO.

YOU AREN'T HALF AS FUNNY AS YOU THINK YOU ARE.

OLD DOC SHMUCK TOOK SOME DNA SAMPLES OUT OF COCOONED AYLEE WAY BACK DURING THE KIKI-VIRUS FIASCO. FIGURED HE'D PULL SOMETHING LIKE THIS, THE IDIOT.
DR. SCHMUCK! DR. SCHMUCK!
THAT EXPLAINS IT. HE COULDN'T GET HIS DATA TO RECONCILE IF HE SAMPLED IT WHILE AYLEE WAS FORM-SHIFTING. DUH.
I GUESS WITH ALL THAT INFLATABLE TECHNOLOGY, MAYBE HIS HEAD'S FULL OF HOT AIR.
IF I TOLD AYLEE WHAT HE WAS UP TO, I THINK SHE'D MAKE AN EXCEPTION ON HER "NO EATING HUMANS" RULE. SO I DON'T THINK WE HAVE ANYTHING TO WORRY ABOUT FROM OLD DR. SCHLOCK!
IF IT WEREN'T FOR HIS INFLATABLE TIME MACHINE, WE'D STILL BE TRAPPED IN THE PAST, TORG. SO STOP BEING SO MEAN, YOU GUYS.
SIGH! I'M USED TO IT.
I'M HAVING TROUBLE GETTING YOUR INFLATABLE CREDIT CARD TO SWIPE THROUGH THE MACHINE.
SERVICE, I SAY! SERVICE!
CHEESEBURGER RITA!

LOOK AT THE TIME!
WHAT AM I? SUPERMAN?
CRASH!
IF I DON'T GET A GREAT JOB OR APPROVED FOR SOME STUDENT LOANS, I'M NOT GOING TO MAKE ANOTHER SEMESTER!
I COULD USE A JOB TOO. BEING A FREELANCE BUM IS CHALLENGING AND ALL, BUT IT'S ALSO HIGH-STRESS I NEED A NEW GIG. SOMETHING MORE RESERVED. ORDERED. TRANQUIL.
SLUGGY FREELANCE

HEY, GUYS!
SO, WANT TO BE A GUINEA PIG FOR MY NEW AND IMPROVED DIMENSIONAL FLUX AGITATOR?
BRING IT ON! BOOYA!

OH, NO! NOT THAT THING AGAIN.
TORG, AS YOU KNOW, MY DIMENSIONAL FLUX AGITATOR CAUSES A RIFT IN RANDOM REALITY PATHS ALLOWING US TO CROSS OVER TO ANOTHER DIMENSION.

BUT THIS TIME, YOU DON'T HAVE TO WORRY ABOUT GETTING STUCK, SINCE THIS REMOTE WILL OPEN A PORTAL BACK!
I HELPED MAKE IT!
POING

YOU WANT TO COME TOO, BUN-BUN?
THE WAY HIS INVENTIONS WORK? THE SAFEST PLACE TO BE IS ON YOUR SHOULDER, WITH THAT THING POINTING AT ME.
SUIT YOURSELF!

IMMEDIATELY UPON ARRIVAL, USE THAT REMOTE TO OPEN A PORTAL HOME. ONCE WE KNOW THAT WORKS, YOU CAN HAVE SOME FUN.

FUN? I THINK THEY'RE INSANE. SHOULDN'T THEY DO THIS FROM RIFF'S LAB? AYLEE'S TRYING TO RUN A BUSINESS HERE!
DO YOU THINK IT'S GOING TO WORK?

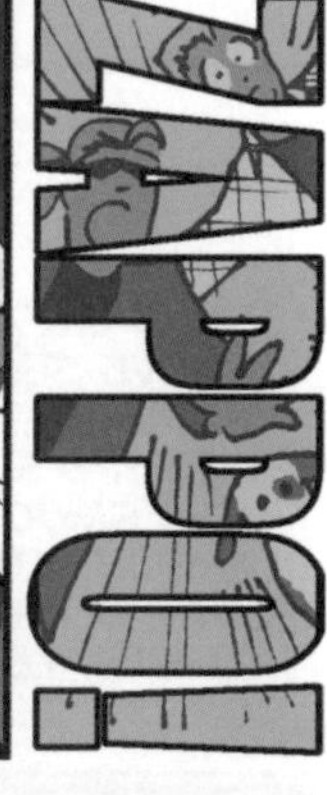
ZAPPO!

NEAT!
WHAT WAS THAT?
WERE ALL THREE OF THEM SUPPOSED TO GO?
I DON'T THINK SO.
THEY'LL OPEN A PORTAL HOME RIGHT AWAY, SO THERE IS NOTHING TO WORRY ABOUT.

THREE HOURS LATER:
OK, NOW WE CAN WORRY. MAYBE RIFF FORGOT THE BATTERIES FOR THE REMOTE.
CAN YOU GET THEM BACK, SASHA?
THE REMOTE IS SYNCHRONIZED WITH THE BASE UNIT, SO IF I MOVE IT TO FIDDLE WITH IT, THEY WON'T BE ABLE TO USE THE REMOTE AT ALL. THEN IT WOULD ALL BE UP TO ME, AND I CAN'T TAKE THAT CHANCE. WE JUST HAVE TO WAIT.

FIVE HOURS LATER:
I DON'T KNOW WHAT TO DO! HALF OF ME IS CONSUMED WITH WORRY OVER TORG AND THE OTHERS.

THE OTHER HALF WANTS TO SAY FIVE HOURS IS WAY TOO LONG FOR YOUR BREAK, GWYNN!
I'LL GET RIGHT BACK TO WORK, ATTILA.
I HOPE THEY DIDN'T WIND UP IN A DIMENSION OF PAIN AGAIN OR SOMETHING.

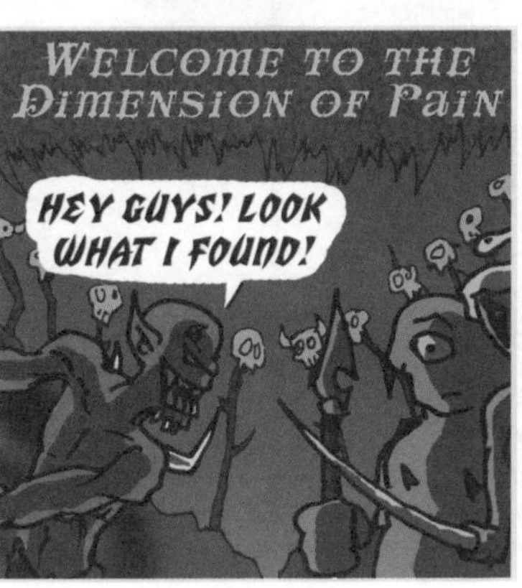
WELCOME TO THE DIMENSION OF PAIN
HEY GUYS! LOOK WHAT I FOUND!

SPARE CHANGE OF EVIL!
SEARCHING UNDER THE CUSHIONS OF THE SOFA OF WICKEDNESS, WERENT YOU.

SO, ANYWAY, NEVER MIND.
I STILL DON'T HAVE A GOOD FEELING ABOUT THIS.

TORG AND BUN-BUN, PREPARE TO BE FLUXED TO ANOTHER DIMENSION VIA MY ALL-NEW DIMENSIONAL FLUX AGITATOR!

ZAPO!

I DIDN'T KNOW YOU WERE COMING!
ME EITHER.
WE ARE **TOTALLY** FLUXED.

wrrrrrrrrr
TORG, NOW ACTIVATE THAT REMOTE TO OPEN A PORTAL HOME.
A-ONE AND-A-TWO AND-A...

BZAPPY!

THIS GREAT BIG NEWS SEGMENT BROUGHT TO YOU BY STEPH'S BLARG. THE SMOOTHEST BLARG AROUND. WHEN YOU'RE BLARG-FACED, IT'S STEPH'S BLARG, OR IT'S GENETICS!

BREAKING NEWS AT **GRITTY CITY! *A RABBIT AND TWO ZORGON SPIES*** WERE APPREHENDED IN AN ATTEMPT TO SABOTAGE **CITY HALL** JUST DAYS BEFORE THE MILITARY SUMMIT WHERE THE **CASCADE MISSILE** IS TO BE UNVEILED!

THE CASCADE MISSILE IS RUMORED TO HAVE ***PLANET-BUSTING*** CAPABILITIES, AND MANY FEAR IT FALLING INTO ZORGON HANDS. SO YOU CAN COUNT ON GOFOTRON TO BE CLOSE AT HAND AND KEEP THE PEACE! ***GO-GO-GOFOTRON!*** NEXT UP: THE LATEST IN QUILTING TECHNOLOGY!

WAY TO PULL AN INTERNATIONAL INCIDENT, GUYS.
WE'RE IN TROUBLE! WE **NEED** THE REMOTE!
WE WON'T BE ABLE TO OPEN THE PORTAL HOME WITHOUT IT.
ZBCP 5392
NOT **THAT** REMOTE! THE ONE FOR THE TV! WATCHING A QUILTING SEGMENT IS CRUEL AND UNUSUAL PUNISHMENT!

GRITTY CITY PRISON OFFICE:
ZORGON SCUM! **HERE!** SO CLOSE TO THE SUMMIT! COMMISSIONER, **TRIPLE** THE BOUNTY ON EVERY POTENTIAL ZORGON TERRORIST, SPY, AND PICKPOCKET **ON THIS PLANET!**
MAYOR, YOU ARE OVERREACTING. WE HAVE THE MALICIOUS ELEMENT WELL UNDER CONTROL.
BLARG

THE SPIES WE HAVE MIGHT NOT EVEN **BE** ZORGONS. THEIR TECHNOLOGY IS STRANGE. TAKE THIS REMOTE FOR INSTANCE.
OK! LATER, SPEED RACER!

NEXT TIME PUT ME IN A CELL WITH THE BARS CLOSER TOGETHER.

AND QUADRUPLE THE STANDARD BOUNTY ON THAT RABBIT.
I'M ON IT, MAYOR!

I GOT THE REMOTE. PUSH WHATEVER BUTTONS YOU HAVE TO AND GET ME HOME.
THE PORTAL OPENS UP AT THE EXACT POINT WE ARRIVED, SO IT WON'T WORK HERE.
SHHHH! PATROL BOT!

WE'RE NOT GOING TO BE WALTZING INTO CITY HALL'S HIGHLY RESTRICTED AREA WHILE A GALACTIC MILITARY SUMMIT IS UNDERWAY. AT LEAST NOT UNTIL I KNOW THE LAY OF THE LAND. YOU GUYS STAY HERE AND LAY LOW UNTIL THE SUMMIT ENDS. I'LL BE ON RECON.

YOU'RE NOT COMING BACK FOR US, ARE YOU, BUN-BUN?
I COULD TAKE YOU WITH ME, TORG!

I'D HAVE TO PULL YOU THROUGH THE BARS. IT'D KIND OF BE LIKE PUSHING PLAY-DOH THROUGH A SIEVE. NEAT!
TELL EVERYONE I SAID "HI" WHEN YOU GET HOME!

DON'T WALK RUN!
XXX VIDEO STORE
drink GUN BUSTER
OTAKOOKS BAR

THIS CITY SEEMS LIKE A COOL PLACE TO BE AND WE'RE STUCK BEHIND THESE BARS FOR THE REST OF OUR LIVES.
NOPE. WE'RE GETTING OUT OF HERE TOMORROW.

YOU GOT A JAILBREAK-PLAN?
NO, THEY'RE SHIPPING US OFF TO THE OUT-WORLD MINES.
JUDGE BOT 2000
YOUR SENTENCE

EXTRA! EXTRA! MILITARY SUMMIT BEGINS.
XTRA

EXTRA! EXTRA! GOLA THE ZORGON LEADER PLANS TO STEAL CASCADE MISSILE!
XTRA

EXTRA! EXTRA! ZORGON GOLA SENDS MONSTER TO DESTROY CITY HALL!

KEE-RUNCH!

jAiL-bREAK... ImMA-nEnT...
NOW THAT IS FAST REPORTING.
I WAS THINKING "BREAKING NEWS"!

YOUR PRINCESS PRINCESS-PRINCESS SAYS: HELP US DEFEAT THE ZORGONS!
"IT'S NEAT!"
SLUGGY FREELANCE

JAILBREAK!

TORG, IN THE FUTURE, WE SNEAK OUT OF PRISON. THIS IS A JAILBREAK, NOT A FOOD FIGHT.
SPEAKING OF FOOD-FIGHTS, THAT IS ONE BIG BROCCOLI!
WHO'S GOING TO SAVE GRITTY-CITY?

IT'S GOFOTRON!

GO-GO-GO-FO-FO-TRON, FIGHT MO' FOE, YOU GO-GO-GO... FO...TRON!*
*OFFICIAL GOFOTRON THEME!

LOOKS LIKE ANOTHER ONE OF GOLA'S MONSTERS, SECRET ANGEL PRINCESS-PRINCESS!
LET'S USE THE GARDENING TOOLS ON THIS VEGETABLE. SECRET LEADER WEATHERMAN!

GO-FO-HOE!

Chunk

IS THAT ALL YOU GOT, GOFOTRON? I COUNTER WITH VEGY-MIGHT!

THIS BATTLE LEAVES A STRANGE AFTERTASTE! NOW I'M STEAMED, SECRET OPS SYSOP!
ROOT-ROOT-RUTABAGA!

WE HAVE NO CHOICE! LET'S DO THAT COOL MOVE THAT WINS THE BATTLE!
SNOORF! OF COURSE! ACTIVATING "COOL MOVE"!

GOFOTRON-COOL-MOVE-THAT-WINS-BATTLE-HA!

slice slice slice

BLORsh

GO-GO-GO-FO-FO-TRON, FIGHT MO' FOE...

SPLAT.

"WELCOME TO GRITTY CITY. MY NAME'S LODOZE. I'M A PART-TIME BOUNTY HUNTER WHO MOONLIGHTS IN SAVING THE UNIVERSE AND IS A FULL TIME MAJOR MALE. I'M TOUGHER THAN A VOLBLARIAN SPACE WORM."

BLAMOBLAMMOBLAMMO

"TAKE THESE SNIPER SHOTS FOR EXAMPLE. I'LL HEAL THESE OUT IN FIVE SECONDS."

"SOME BLARG -FACED YOUTH BLASTING INTO TRAFFIC FOR FUN. I REMEMBER BEING THAT AGE. BUT NOBODY DOES THAT TO THE MAJOR MALE!"

"THE GIFT-WRAPPING IS A NEW THING. THERE'S ALWAYS A BIG COINAGE BONUS FOR BRINGING BACK THE BOUNTY IN ONE PIECE, AND THAT'S NOT EASY WITH THEM HANGING OFF THE BACK OF MY BIKE BY THEIR RETINA CORDS. THE PADDED BOXES HAVE BEEN PADDING MY POCKETS WITH COINAGE. AND DON'T FORGET THE CARDS!"

WARNING:
THE FOLLOWING
COMIC CONTAINS
GRAPHIC
VIOLENCE.
LODOZE STYLE
STARRING:
LOTS-O-BLOOD.
TIME PERMITTING:
NOSE-PICKING
VIEWER'S
DISCRETION IS
ADVISED.

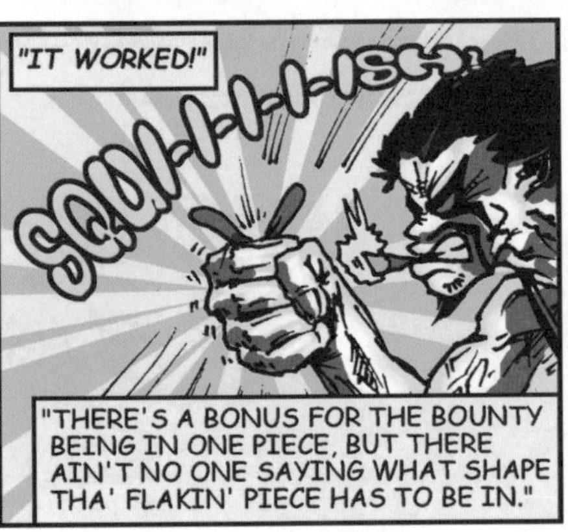

FUN-RABBIT-FACTS: RABBITS ARE FLEXIBLE, ABLE TO SQUEEZE BEHIND FURNITURE AND INTO OTHER SMALL AREAS YOU WOULDN'T EXPECT.

WOW! WE HAVEN'T DONE A FUN RABBIT FACT SINCE 1998 WHEN WE COMMENTED ON A RABBIT'S RAZOR-SHARP CLAWS!

SO HERE WE ARE. BACK IN THE SAME CELL WE WERE IN A WEEK AGO.
GREAT BIG
ZGCP 5392

GOOD THING THEY NEVER FIXED IT!

"THIS JUST IN! THOSE ZORGON SPIES HAVE ESCAPED GRITTY CITY PRISON AGAIN! THE GRITTY CITY COMMISSIONER HAS BEEN FOUND STRANGLED AFTER A SERIES OF KICKS TO THE BUTTOCKS, BUT EVIDENCE POINTS TO THE MAYOR, NOT THE SPIES!"

WE DON'T HAVE A LOT OF TIME. I'VE GOT TO FAMILIARIZE MYSELF WITH CURRENT SECURITY SYSTEMS IF I'M GOING TO GET US INTO CITY HALL.
WOW! I HAD NO IDEA THIS PLANET WAS SO SMALL!
SLEUTH BOT BOOTH

"THIRD PLANET FROM THE SUN IN THE GRITTANIA SYSTEM. GRITTANIA 3 EARNS THE NICKNAME "GRITTY CITY" FOR BEING ONE OF THE POOREST CRIME-RIDDLED PLANETS IN THE LOHVO PROTECTORATE"

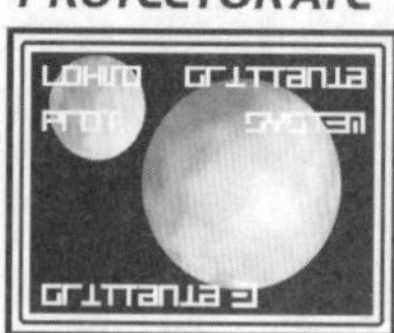

THE LOHVOS ARE...

THE BLUE ANIME-LOOKING PEOPLE ALL OVER THE PLACE. WHAT GOT ME CURIOUS IS, IF THIS PLANET IS SUCH A DUMP, WHY HAVE AN INTERGALACTIC MILITARY SUMMIT HERE?

OMINOUS MOOD ENHANCEMENT: 5 COINAGE.
PAY THE BOT, TORG.

WITH THE "GRITTY CITY" MILITARY SUMMIT COMING TO A SUCCESSFUL CLOSE, THE HOLD ON INTERSTELLAR TRAVEL FROM THE GRITTANIA SYSTEM WILL BE LIFTED SHORTLY!

THERE'S CITY HALL. THAT'S WHERE WE NEED TO BE.

CITY HALL GRITTANIA 3

RIFF, THE SUMMIT JUST ENDED FIVE MINUTES AGO! NOBODY'S LEFT THE BUILDING YET. AREN'T WE HERE A BIT EARLY?
DO YOU THINK BUN-BUN'S GOING TO WAIT LONG?

NO, NOT REALLY.
I TOLD YOU GUYS TO HURRY.
Sorry, boss! Leg cramp.

CITY HALL SECURITY IS DAMN TIGHT, BUT I HAVE A PLAN.
YOU'RE LIMPING, BUN-BUN! WHAT HAPPENED TO YOU?
Da boss got a few busted ribs and a bum leg but you shoulda seen da udder guy!

THE *"BOSS?"* **HEY!** YOU'VE GOT **FLUNKIES!** WHEREDJA GET FLUNKIES?
THIS IS GRITTY-CITY. KICK A CAN, YOU'LL PEG ONE.

DARN IT! I **NEVER** GET FLUNKIES!
I ONLY HAVE ONE FLUNKY AND I'M NOT COMPLAINING.

HEY! YOU BETTER BE TALKING ABOUT KIKI!
Dis bum kicked a can at me 'ead. Want me ta be yer flunky and squash 'im for ye?

THERE'S A JUNCTION BOX HERE. RIFF, YOU KNOW HOW IT TICKS?
ENOUGH TO SHUT DOWN THE SECURITY CANNONS BUT NOT ENOUGH TO STOP THE ALARM IT'LL TRIGGER.
THAT'S WHERE YOU COME IN, GUPPY. YOU'RE GOING TO...
HEY! WHAT ABOUT ME? WHAT DO **I** DO?

YOU WATCH OUR BACKS, NERD-BOY. (WAY BACK). I TOOK THIS GUN OFF SOME WUSS BOUNTY HUNTER; IT SHOULD BE POWERFUL ENOUGH TO HANDLE ANYTHING THEY THROW AT YOU.

PRISONER TRANSPORT SHIP FIVE NOW DEPARTING FOR OUTER-WORLD MINES.
BOY, THAT GUN SURE HAD SOME KICKBACK, DIDN'T IT?
YOU SHOT AT A MOUSE!
WHAT WAS *I* THINKING?

OK, WE'RE CLEARED TO LEAVE PORT. I THOUGHT INTERSTELLAR TRAVEL WAS STILL OFF LIMITS AROUND HERE.
THE MAYOR PULLED SOME STRINGS. HE WANTS THESE PARTICULAR ZORGON SPIES AWAY FROM THE GRITTANIA SYSTEM *ASAP.*
Come to Paradisia

THE ZORGON SPIES WHO BUSTED INTO CITY HALL TWICE? I DIDN'T KNOW WE HAD CELEBRITIES ON BOARD!
SPEAKING OF CELEBRITIES, THE MAYOR ALSO ARRANGED A LITTLE SURPRISE FOR THE ZORGONS.

"SOON AS WE LEAVE ORBIT, **YOUR BUTT IS MINE, BUN-BUN!**"

NO, LIEUTENANT, THE CELEBRITY SURPRISE IS *NOT* PRINCESS-PRINCESS POPPING OUT OF A CAKE. IS THAT YOUR ANSWER FOR EVERYTHING?
ONLY BECAUSE IT *SOLVES* EVERYTHING.

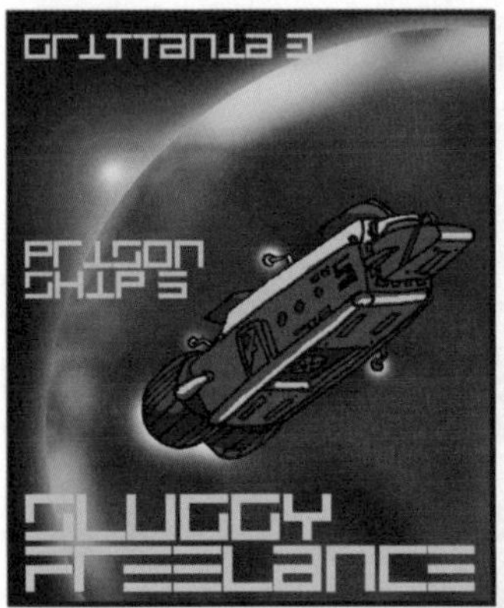

THANKS TO YOU, NERD-BOY, WE'RE ALL GOING TO SPEND FIFTY YEARS WORKING THE MINES.
Nobody lasts fifty years in the mines. We all just got da **death sentence**.
SOMEBODY CALL?

"ONCE I WAS BACK TO MY OLD LODOZE SELF I FOUND OUT BUN-BUN HAD GOT HIMSELF OUT-WORLDED. FIGURED I'D TAG ALONG, AND NOW HE HAS NO-WHERE TO RUN. I THINK I KNOW THE FIRST LESSON BUN-BUN'S GONNA LEARN IN CLASS-LODOZE. **LEAVE MY STUFF ALONE!"**

LOOK WHO'S BACK AMONG THE LIVING? NICE NOSTRIL THERE, *NOSEBLOW.*

"SEE, HE STOLE MY GUN AND I WANTED IT BACK. I LATER LEARNED THAT HE OVER-LOADED THE CLIP-CHARGE AND BLEW IT UP, TAKING PART OF CITY HALL WITH IT. BUT THE MAYOR LOANED ME SOMETHING OF HIS. *THIS!"*

HEY! THE REMOTE!
COULD WE SPEED UP THE INNER DIALOGUE? I ONLY HAVE FIFTY YEARS TO LIFE!

GUESS WHERE I'M GOING TO SHOVE IT?
BY SASHA!

OOH-OOOH!
I know! I know!
I HAVE A RECOMMENDATION!
ALL OF YAS, SHUT YER TRAPS!
AIRLOCK

WHAT THE HELL WAS *THAT?*
SOMETHING HIT US?
THAT WAS A SHOCKWAVE.
AIRLOCK
BEEP

HEY! WHERE'D LODOZE GO?
AIRLOCK
HE HAD TO STEP OUT FOR SOME FRESH AIR.

WE GOT THE REMOTE BACK! NOW ALL WE HAVE TO DO IS GET BACK TO...
RIFF? WHERE'S GRITTY CITY?
THE SHOCKWAVE... SOMEBODY BLEW UP THE PLANET!

ALL THOSE PEOPLE!
THE PORTAL!
Me favorite pub!
IT'S GONE.

WHO COULD HAVE DESTROYED GRITTANIA 3?
CAPTAIN! ZORGON COMMAND DESTROYER OFF PORT SIDE! IT APPEARED OUT OF NOWHERE... LIKE A GHOST!

ALL CHANNELS! THE ZORGONS HAVE VOID-GHOST TECH-NOLOGY AND THE CASCADE MISSILE! THE ZORGONS HAVE DESTROYED GRITTANIA 3! THE ZORGONS HAVE VOID-GHOST TECHNOLOGY AND...

THEY'RE JAMMING US! PART OF THAT MIGHT HAVE GOTTEN OUT. WHAT DO WE DO NOW?
WE'VE DONE OUR DUTY LIKE MEN. NOW IS THE TIME TO CRY LIKE BABIES.

"RIFF? HOW ARE WE GOING TO GET HOME NOW?"

WE ARE ON A HIGHLY CLASSIFIED MISSION, TOO CLASSIFIED EVEN FOR YOU TO INTERFERE WITH. WE KNOW ALL ABOUT YOU, **LORD GRATER**. ALL YOUR SECRETS. DON'T FORCE MY REPORT TO **ZORGON GOLA** TO BE A NEGATIVE ONE.

RHIBB PRIME.
ZORGON HOMEWORLD.

HAIL ZORGON GOLA! YOU CALLED FOR ME, SIR?
THAT FOOL GRATER DESTROYED GRITTANIA 3. THAT ROCK WAS OF NO IMPORTANCE, EVEN TO THE LOHVOS. BUT WE *MUST* KEEP OUR CLOAKING TECH-NOLOGY SECRET.

HAVE OUR SPY NETWORKS ENCOURAGE THE RUMORS THAT WE HAVE THE CASCADE MISSILE, BUT NO SHIPS ARE TO MAKE USE OF CLOAKING UNTIL.... *ARE YOU STARING AT MY LIPS?*
NO SIR!

YOU ARE, AREN'T YOU! DON'T THINK A MAN WEARING LIPSTICK CAN RULE THE ZORGONS, DO YOU?
NO SIR!

DO YOU THINK THE COLOR SUITS ME?
VERY MUCH SO, SIR!

VERY WELL. DISMISSED!
GOD, I WISH HE'D WEAR PANTS!

DESPITE THE MILITARY PRESSING FOR SWIFT RETALIATION OVER THE DESTRUCTION OF GRITTANIA 3, MANY LOHVOS CALL FOR PEACE. WE GO LIVE TO OUR **INTERVIEWBOT** ON THE CAPITAL PLANET OF PARADISIA.
GREAT BIG NEW
YAMA

ALL WE ARE SAYYYING, IS GIVE PEACE A CHANCE!
IF WE BLOW UP A ZORGON WORLD, WE'LL BE AS BAD AS THE ZORGONS.
WHO CARES ABOUT GRITTY CITY? THE ZORGONS SEEM LIKE NICE CHAPS!

AND NOW, FOR THE WEATHER, IT'S **WEATHERMAN STAN!**
THANKS, YAMA!
GRITTANIA 3'S DESTRUCTION IS REALLY MESSING UP OUR SUNNY DAYS! GET ON YOUR SWEAT-REPROCESSORS, PEOPLE OF THE TROPICAL GRITTANIA 2! OR SHOULD I SAY *DESERT* OF GRITTANIA 2? **THAT'S NOT ALL!** EVERYONE IN THE TRI-SYSTEM AREA CAN LOOK FORWARD TO COLDER WINTERS, AND SHORTER SUMMERS! AND EVERYONE'S BEACHFRONT PROPERTY IS GOING TO BE LANDLOCKED OR UNDERWATER!

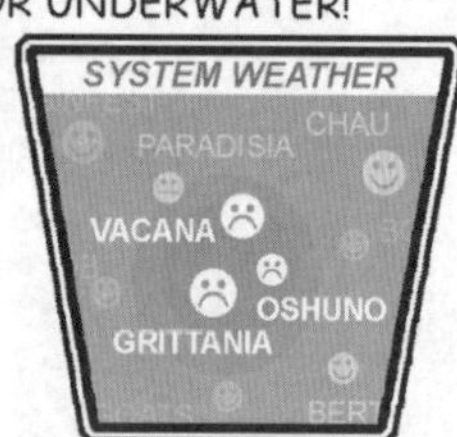
SYSTEM WEATHER
PARADISIA
CHAU
VACANA
OSHUNO
GRITTANIA

DESTROY THE ZORGONS! THE ZORGONS MUST DIE! DESTROY THE ZORGONS! THE ZORGONS MUST DIE!...

PARADISIA
LOHVO HOMEWORLD
GENERAL, WE WILL *NOT* DESTROY A ZORGON PLANET IN RETALIATION! I PUT FAITH IN GOFOTRON!

KING LOHVO PROAN, THE ZORGONS HAVE STOLEN OUR CASCADE MISSILE DESIGNS AND ARE RUMORED TO HAVE VOID-GHOST CLOAKING TECHNOLOGY. WE NEED TO POWER OUR SHIPS WITH GOFOTRON'S PATENTED "AMAZINGLY HASTY DRIVE" AND ARM THOSE SHIPS WITH CASCADE MISSILES IF WE ARE GOING TO KEEP UP, LET ALONE HAVE VENGEANCE.

GOFOTRON WILL SEEK **JUSTICE,** NOT VENGEANCE, GENERAL BENEDICT! AND THE PEOPLE STAND BEHIND *GOFOTRON*.
I MEAN NO DISRESPECT, PRINCESS-PRINCESS BUT THE PEOPLE ARE TURNING AGAINST YOUR FATHER AND GOFOTRON. LOOK WHAT I FOUND AT THE MALL!
BEAM ME UP, CHACHI! THERE'S NO INTELLIGENT LIFE IN GRITTY CITY THANKS TO GOFOTRON AND KING PROAN!

MY GOD, IT'S TRUE!
JUST BUMPED THE *"IF YOU CAN READ THIS YOU'RE TOO CLOSE TO MY BOOBS"* SHIRT FOR TOP SELLERS!

SLUGGY FREELANCE

ARE YOU SURE YOU DON'T WANT TO STAY, PRINCESS-PRINCESS? YOUR FATHER, KING LOHVO PROAN IS GOING TO BE CONTACTING SECRET ANGEL PRINCESS-PRINCESS OF THE GOFOTRON TEAM!
I HAVE A PRIOR ENGAGEMENT, BUTLER-SAN!

GO-GO-GOFOTRON!

LITTLE DOES ANYONE KNOW THAT PRINCESS-PRINCESS *IS* SECRET ANGEL PRINCESS-PRINCESS!

THAT SOUNDS REALLY STUPID WHEN I SAY IT OUT LOUD.

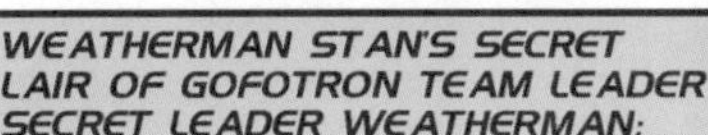

WEATHERMAN STAN'S SECRET LAIR OF GOFOTRON TEAM LEADER SECRET LEADER WEATHERMAN:

WE OF TEAM GOFOTRON HAVE DECIDED THE LOHVO MILITARY DOES NOT HAVE THE WISDOM TO USE OUR ASTONISHING **AMAZINGLY HASTY DRIVE**. YOU ARE NOT WISE LIKE US, GENERAL BENEDICT! ONLY GOFOTRON SHALL BE AMAZINGLY HASTY. SECRET LEADER WEATHERMAN, OUT.
beep!

THANKS FOR HOLDING, SECRET ANGEL PRINCESS-PRINCESS! WE NEED TO TALK...
HEY, MR. "WISE", IT'S STILL THE GENERAL. YOU HAVE TO TAP THE FLASH BUTTON TWICE.

I KNOW, I WAS JUST... TESTING YOUR KNOWLEDGE. YOU MAY EVENTUALLY BE WISE ENOUGH TO LEARN THE SECRETS OF GOFOTRON.
TAP. TAP.

GENERAL BENEDICT KEEPS MAKING FUN OF ME!
YES! I AM! THERE *IS* NO FLASH BUTTON, IDIOT! GIMMIE THE AMAZINGLY HASTY DRIVE ALREADY!

LORD GRATER'S COMMAND SHIP:
CHECK THIS OUT! I FIGURED OUT WHY THERE ARE NO STARS AROUND HERE. ONLY PLANETS AND NEIGHBORING SUNS. SEE HOW CLOSE TOGETHER EVERYTHING IS?
LIBRARY — DATA

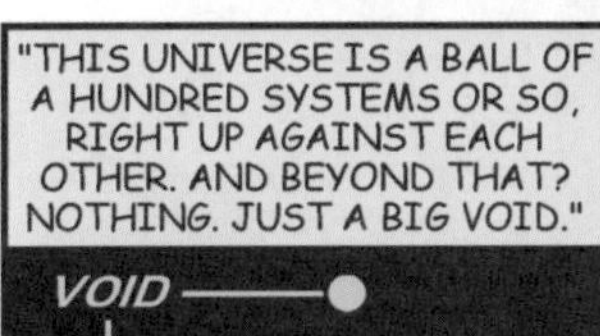

"THIS UNIVERSE IS A BALL OF A HUNDRED SYSTEMS OR SO, RIGHT UP AGAINST EACH OTHER. AND BEYOND THAT? NOTHING. JUST A BIG VOID."

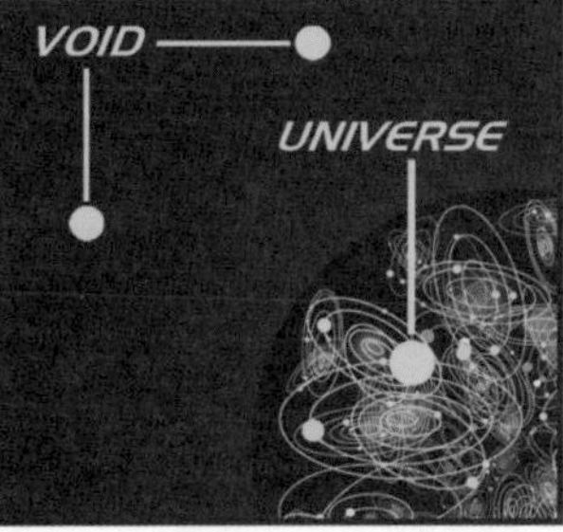

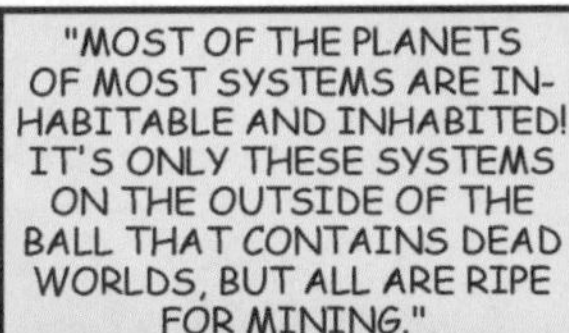

"MOST OF THE PLANETS OF MOST SYSTEMS ARE INHABITABLE AND INHABITED! IT'S ONLY THESE SYSTEMS ON THE OUTSIDE OF THE BALL THAT CONTAINS DEAD WORLDS, BUT ALL ARE RIPE FOR MINING."

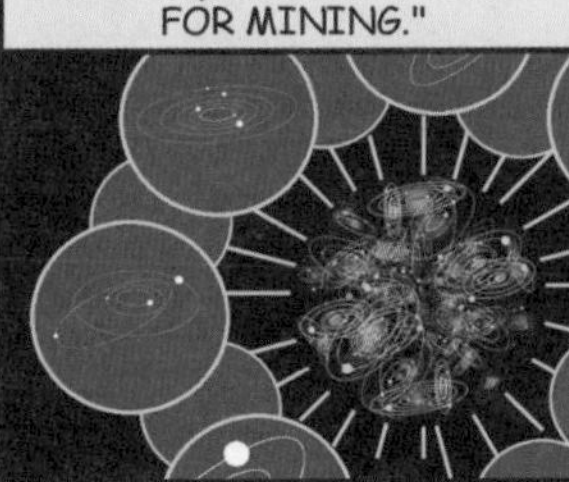

THE OUT-WORLD MINES WE ALMOST WOUND UP ON!
EXACTLY. I'VE NEVER SEEN A UNIVERSE SO ...DELIBERATE.
IT'S NOT A UNIVERSE AT ALL! IT'S A *PUNYVERSE!*

BECAUSE IT'S...UM... PUNY AND STUFF.
YOU DONE?
YES!

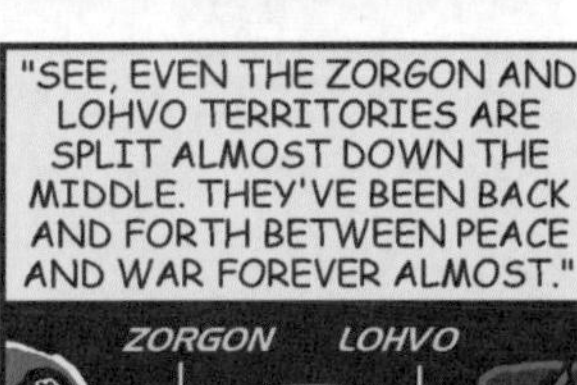

"SEE, EVEN THE ZORGON AND LOHVO TERRITORIES ARE SPLIT ALMOST DOWN THE MIDDLE. THEY'VE BEEN BACK AND FORTH BETWEEN PEACE AND WAR FOREVER ALMOST."

HOW DOES ANY OF THIS HELP US GET HOME?
THIS REMOTE WILL OPEN A PORTAL AT THE POINT IT BELIEVED WE ARRIVED ON PARALLEL EARTH, TAKING IN CONSIDERATION ROTATION AND ORBIT. SO WHEREVER THAT PART OF CITY HALL WOULD HAVE BEEN IF GRITTANIA 3 WASN'T DESTROYED, THAT'S WHERE THE PORTAL WOULD BE. ONCE I HAVE A GOOD IDEA, WE JUST HAVE TO SNEAK BACK INTO THE GRITTANIA SYSTEM.

SECRET LEADER WEATHERMAN, IT'S REALLY ME! **SECRET ANGEL PRINCESS-PRINCESS!**
YOU'RE GENERAL BENEDICT IN A DRESS! I CAN **TELL!**

I'M NOT WEARING A DRESS! I'M WEARING A FORM-FITTING GOFOTRON UNIFORM!
NOW **THAT** GOT MY ATTENTION!

WE WILL **NOT** DESTROY A ZORGON PLANET IN VENGEANCE. BUT WE **WILL** USE GOFOTRON FOR GREAT JUSTICE. WE'LL PUNISH THOSE RESPONSIBLE.

ALERT THE TEAM. **WE'RE GOING TO DESTROY LORD GRATER AND THE ENTIRE CREW OF HIS COMMAND SHIP.**
DON'T YOU WANT TO KNOW WHAT I'M WEARING?

LORD GRATER HAS LOST INTEREST IN US AS SPIES, AND WE HAVE BEEN ABSORBED AS PRIVATES INTO THE ZORGON ARMY. THIS WILL MAKE GETTING BACK TO THE GRITTANIA SYSTEM DIFFICULT, THANKS TO GOFOTRON.

SPIES HAVE INFORMED US THAT GOFOTRON IS ON ITS WAY TO DESTROY US, AND THE WORD FROM LORD GRATER IS THAT EVERYONE WILL FIGHT. A HUNDRED OF OUR PILOTED BATTLE-BOTS AGAINST THEIR ONE BIG BOT. DESPITE THE ODDS IN OUR FAVOR, WE ARE ALMOST SURE TO LOSE. LORD GRATER'S BRAVERY WILL LIVE ON IN ZORGON POETRY, THEY SAY.

PLEASE, GOLA? PLEEEEEESE CAN WE USE THE CLOAKING DEVICE?
THANKS TO YOU AND THE GRITTANIA 3 DEBACLE, THERE ARE ALREADY RUMORS THAT WE HAVE A CLOAKING DEVICE. I WILL NOT HAVE THEM CONFIRMED.

WE HAVE THE CASCADE MISSILE PLANS FROM YOU, SO YOU ARE EXPEN... ARE YOU STARING AT MY LIPS?
YEAH. DO THEY HURT? DID A BEE STING YOU?

ZORGON POETRY WEEKLY:

Ode to Lord Grater's Bravery

Brave to battle
Gofotron
Brave to not
withdraw
Brave to try and
walk around
With his foot
wedged in his
maw.

PILOTS, THIS IS THE 2-WING-PHU TRANSBOT. YOU ARE CURRENTLY IN BOT-MODE, GOOD FOR SUBTLE CLOSE MANEUVERING AND BOT-COMBAT. THERE IS ALSO FIGHTER-MODE, FOR FAST STRIKES AND DISTANCE ATTACKS. MY JOB IS TO MAKE SURE YOU MASTER BOTH MODES.
PILOTING TRANSBOTS FOR DUMMIES SEMINAR

TEACH? WHAT ABOUT THIS MODE BUTTON TO THE RIGHT OF THE FIGHTER BUTTON? WHAT MODE IS THAT?
THAT IS RESTRICTED. YOU ARE NOT AUTHORIZED TO PRESS THAT BUTTON.
BUT... NOW I GOTTA KNOW WHAT IT DOES!
IMPORTANT: PLEASE KEEP HANDS AWAY DURING TRANS-IFIZATION.

PRIVATE TORG, DON'T MAKE ME SEND YOU TO THE REEDUCATION CLAMPS.
DON'T YOU MEAN REEDUCATION "CAMPS"?
NOPE.
I'LL BE GOOD.

YOU FLYING WITH ME?
YOU THINK I WANT TO RIDE WITH NERD-BOY?
WHATEVER.
WHAT'S THE HOLD-UP ANYWAY?
DON'T KNOW. GOFOTRON SHOULD HAVE BEEN HERE BY NOW.

THIS IS TAKING TOO LONG!
YOU CAN'T FIGHT EVIL ON AN EMPTY STOMACH. LOOK! A SECRET ANGEL PRINCESS-PRINCESS IN TANK-TOP FIGHTING GEAR DOLL! WITH KUNG-FU GRIP!
SNORF! MY McMINIMEAL CAME WITH A CRAPPY LEADER WEATHERMAN RUB-ON TATTOO!
McBEHEMOTH BURGERS
WHO ORDERED THESE TRIBBLE McNUGGETS? WHERE'S MY SUGAR-FREEZY?
ROOT ROOT ROOT CANAL

LORD GRATER! GOFOTRON APPROACHES!
ALL UNITS SCRAMBLE!

WELL, BOT-MODE IS COOL, BUT YOU WOULD THINK FIGHTER-MODE IS MORE EFFECTIVE IN COMBAT.
SO WHY HAVE IT?
05
06

I THINK I FIGURED THAT OUT. THINK ABOUT HOW MUCH IT WOULD COST AND HOW MUCH SPACE IT WOULD USE TO BUILD ENOUGH RUNWAYS AND HANGARS TO LAUNCH A HUNDRED FIGHTERS QUICKLY.

POING
weee!
NO LIFEBOT ON DUTY
THIS IS FAR MORE ECONOMICAL!

YOU WILL USE FIGHTER-MODE TO CLOSE QUICKLY WITH THE TARGET, AND THEN RELY ON YOUR SQUADS FOR TACTICS. ALL UNITS PREPARE TO BE AUTO-SWITCHED TO FIGHTER MODE.
DEATH TO GOFOTRON! TRANSBOTS... *CHANGEROOO!*

TRANS IN PROGRESS
SNAP! CRACKLE! POP!

LET'S PARTY!

BOY, DID *I* PICK THE WRONG TIME TO CHANGE THE CD.

FIGHTER-MODE SUCKS! LET'S GO BACK TO BOT-MODE.
CAN'T. WE'RE ON AUTOMATIC UNTIL WE REACH GOFOTRON.

COMMAND CONTROL DEVICE
WARNING: NOT ON TOO TIGHT.

EVERYTHING HAS A MANUAL.
YANK!

TRANSBOT, CHANGEROO!
SNAP! CRACKLE! POP!

FUEL AT 0%. POWER DROPPING...
LET ME CHECK MY NOTES.
MAYBE I SHOULD'VE RODE WITH NERD-BOY.

UM, RIFF? MY ARMS GOT STUCK IN THE COCKPIT THINGY WHEN WE CHANGED FORM. I'M KIND-OF CAREENING OUT OF CONTROL.
I SO TAKE THAT BACK.

LOOK, TORG, I CAN'T REALLY HELP YOU. I'VE GOT MY OWN PROBLEMS.
I WASN'T AS MUCH LOOKING FOR HELP AS HAVING YOU GET OUT OF THE WAY!

WHAM!

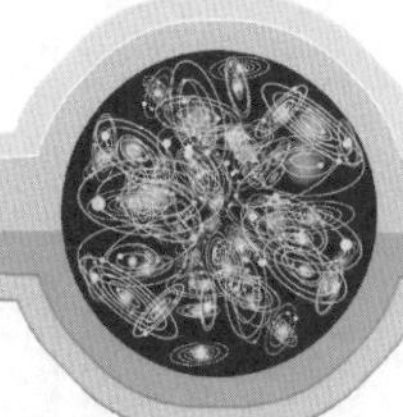

SLUGGY FREELANCE
SECRET LEADER WEATHERMAN! WE HAVE UPWARDS OF A HUNDRED ZORGON TRANSBOTS MOVING IN!
ROOT-ROOT-ROOT-OF-ALL-EVIL!
KEEP TO THE FAR SIDE OF THE PLANET, WE'LL CUT DOWN OUR CHANCES OF BEING OVERWHELMED. KEEP FOCUSED, SECRET OPS SYSOP!

HERE THEY COME. FIRST WAVE.

SLICE

CHOP
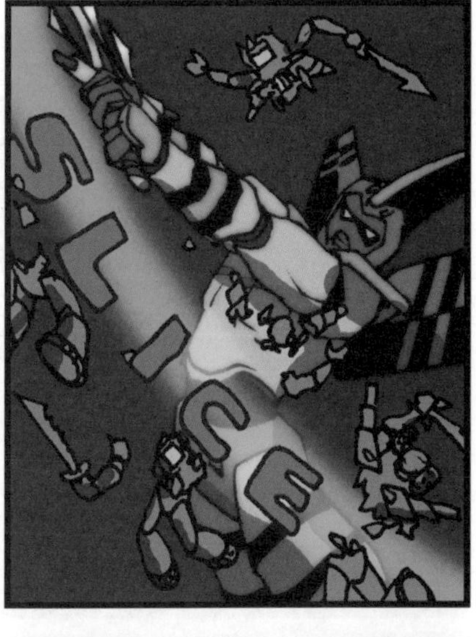
SLICE

TEN ZORGON BOTS AT TEN O'CLOCK!

SLICE

CHOP

SLICE

CHOP

LOOK OUT! snoorf. ZORGONS IN FIGHTER-MODE!

ZAP
ZAP
ZAP

BOOM!
BOOM!
BOOM!

FOURTEEN MORE BOTS AT SIX!

SLICE

TING

CHOP

CHOP

SLICE

CHOP

SLICE

SNORF! *MORE* ZORGONS IN FIGHTER MODE!

ZAP
ZAP
ZAP

BOOM!
BOOM!
BOOM!

SIXTY-SEVEN BOTS COMING AT US FROM ALL DIRECTIONS!

CHOP

SLICE

CHOP

SLICE

TING

CHOP

SLICE

TING

SLICE

CHOP

TING

SLICE

TING

SLICE

SNORF! *MORE* ZORGONS IN FIGHTER MODE!

ZAP
ZAP
ZAP

BOOM!
BOOM!
BOOM!

TING

SLICE

CHOP

SLICE

CHOP

TING

SLASH

SLICE

CHOP

HOLD UP A SECOND.
CRAMP.

URK Ahhhh
THAT'LL DO.

SLASH

SLICE

TING

SLICE

CHOP

SLASH

CHOP

TING

SLICE

CHOP

GO-GO-GOFOTRON!

WELL DONE, TEAM!

SNORF! *MORE* ZORGONS IN FIGHTER MODE!

NO, SNOORF. THERE ARE NO MORE ZORGONS.

SNORF! *MORE* ZORGONS IN FIGHTER MODE!

TIME TO BREAK OUT THE SECRET SNOORFY SNOORF-SNOORF MUZZLE.

I'll be good.

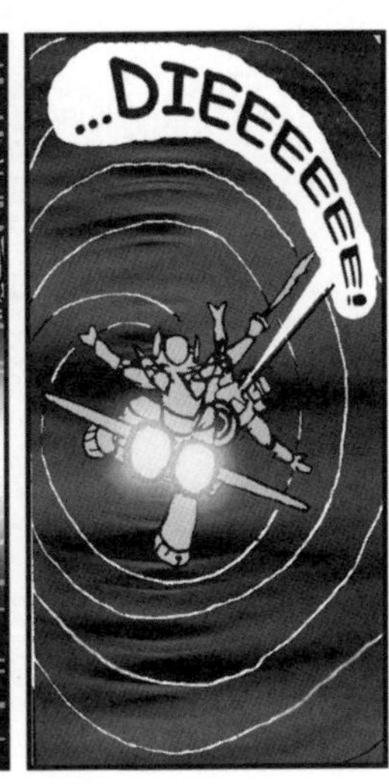

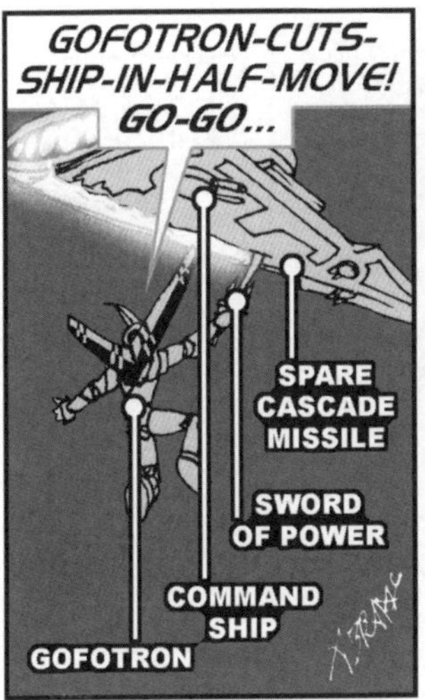

IN TODAY'S NEWS: GOFOTRON SUCCEEDED IN DESTROYING THE VILLAINOUS ZORGON LORD GRATER AND HIS COMMAND SHIP. IN THE PROCESS, AN EXPLOSION SERIOUSLY DAMAGED THE ROBOT.

A MASSIVE SEARCH PARTY IS SEARCHING FOR THE MISSING **SECRET ANGEL PRINCESS-PRINCESS** AS WELL AS **GOFOTRON'S RIGHT ARM**. OUR PRAYERS GO OUT FOR THEM BOTH. BUT MORE FOR SECRET ANGEL, SINCE SHE'S A PERSON AND GOFOTRON'S ARM IS A THING. BUT THEN AGAIN, I'M, A THING, SO WHO CARES. NOBODY CARES ABOUT US THINGS.

I HATE YOU ALL.

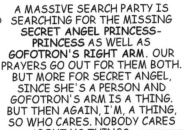

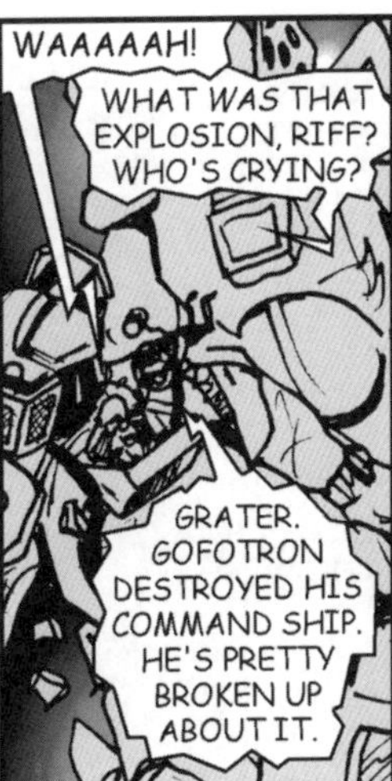

MY KING, I'M SORRY TO HEAR THAT THE PRINCESS IS MISSING. SHE PROBABLY IS OFF MOURNING THE LOSS OF SECRET ANGEL PRINCESS-PRINCESS, AS ARE WE ALL. BUT I HAVE GRAVE NEWS ABOUT THE FATE OF YOUR ENTIRE KINGDOM.

HEY, RIFF, DID YOU NOTICE HOW GOFOTRON'S ARM SEEMS SHORTER? LIKE IT TELESCOPED DOWN?

YEAH. NOTICE HOW THE ARMPIT BLEW OUT LIKE AN ENGINE CORE? AND THOSE POSSIBLE LANDING-GEAR HOUSINGS? IT LOOKS LIKE THIS BOT ARM COULD TURN ITSELF INTO AN INCONSPICUOUS...

GUYS?
I KNOW ABOUT YOU, I KNOW ABOUT GOFOTRON, AND I HAVE A HASTY DRIVE, AND MY ENEMY'S DAUGHTER IN MY POSSESSION! ONCE I GET THIS TO ZORGON GOLA, A ZORGON VICTORY IS ENSURED!
HEY, GUYS?
THEN, I WILL MAKE SURE THAT YOU DON'T SURVIVE!

GUYS! WHAT'S THAT MOON-SIZED THING WITH THE TEETH HEADING THIS WAY?

ZORGON FOOL! THAT'S NO MOON! THAT'S A THING WITH TEETH AND IT'S HEADING THIS WAY!
HEY!
IT'S A VOLBLARIAN SPACE WORM! IT'S GOING TO SWALLOW US WHOLE!

LET'S MAKE USE OF THAT HASTY DRIVE THINGY AND GET OUT OF HERE!
HER ENGINE'S TOAST. WE COULD ALL PILE INTO TORG'S TRANSBOT. IT'S THE ONLY THING THAT MOVES AROUND HERE.

AS SOON AS TORG HITS THE GAS, THE ENERGY SIGNATURE WILL CAUSE THE VOLBLARIAN SPACE WORM TO POUNCE. IT CAN MOVE VERY QUICKLY IF IT THINKS ITS DINNER IS GETTING AWAY.

WHAT ABOUT WEAPONS?
ONLY MY GOFOCANNON IS CAPABLE OF DETERRING SOMETHING THAT BIG! BUT THE COMPUTER GOT FRIED IN THE EXPLOSION, AND THE COMPUTER CONTROLS THE GUNS!

EVERYTHING HAS A MANUAL. TORG? SUIT UP!

WHOA!
BE CAREFUL! LOSE YOUR GRIP AND IT'S OVER!
GOTCHA, RIFF!

JUST LIKE FOLLOWING A ROADMAP. ...AND THE ACTIVATION POINT IS...

HERE!

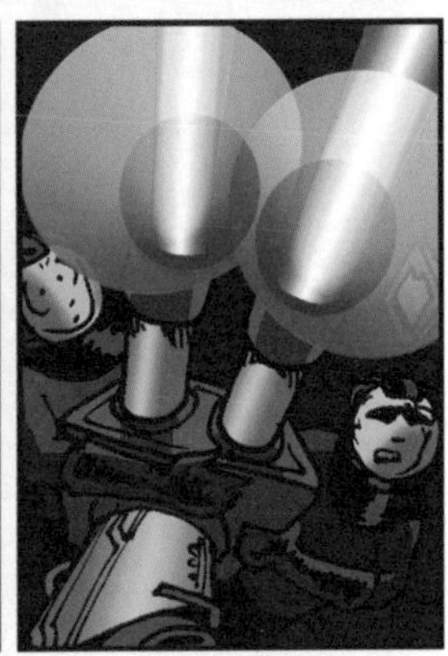

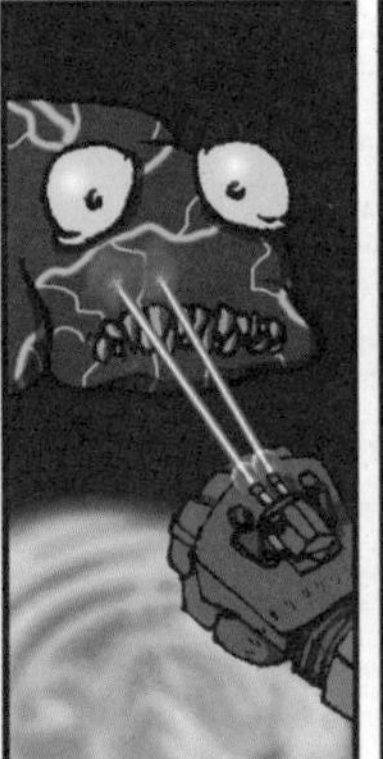

YIPE! YIPE! YIPE!

YES!
UP TOP!

NOTE TO SELF: HIGH-FIVING IS DANGEROUS IN A ZERO-G ENVIRONMENT.

SLUGGY FREELANCE

NOW WITH YOUR BOYS FLOATING OFF HELPLESSLY IN SPACE, YOU ARE DEFENSELESS, LORD GRATER!

GO-GO-COMBAT-STYLE!

POST-TEEN PUNCHING POWER PRINCESS
POST-TEEN PUNCHING POWER PRINCESS

POST-TEEN PUNCHING POWER PRINCESS

HERO IN A HALTER-TOP

*SUNG TO THE TUNE OF THE TEENAGE MUTANT NINJA TURTLES THEME SONG

YOU KNOW I'VE BEEN A DARK LORD FOR YEARS AND I STILL DON'T HAVE A THEME SONG. EXCEPT FOR THAT ONE TIME...
bzzzt
wrn

HERE. HE. COMES. LORD GRATER. LORD GRATER. HE'S. SMART. ER. THAN-A. SMALL. PO-TA-TER.*

*SUNG TO THE TUNE OF THE IMPERIAL MARCH FROM THE EMPIRE STRIKES BACK

THEY HAD TO MISPRONOUNCE "POTATO" TO GET IT TO RHYME. THERE WASN'T ENOUGH OBOE. I WASN'T VERY HAPPY WITH IT AT ALL.
wrn

IN ANY CASE, LET "MY BOYS" DRIFT OFF IN SPACE. I NEVER NEEDED THEM, AND I SURE DON'T NEED THEM TO DEFEAT THE LIKES OF YOU!
wrn

WHAM!

WHAM!

WHAM!

WHAM!

LET'S GET SOMETHING STRAIGHT. THEY ARE **MY** BOYS AND WE ARE RETRIEVING THEM.
GRAVITY CONTROL
up
down
I FELL ON MY KEYS

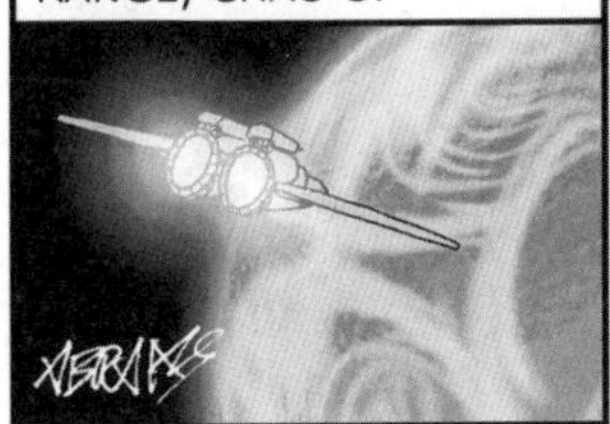
AND SO, BUN-BUN TOOK CONTROL OF THE SITUATION, RIFF AND TORG WERE RETRIEVED, AND EVERYONE PILED INTO TORG'S TRANSBOT IN FIGHTER MODE. THEY FLEW OFF TO THE ONLY INHABITED PLANET WITHIN THEIR LIMITED TRAVEL AND COMMUNICATIONS RANGE, CHAU-5.

CHAU-5? THEY **EAT** PEOPLE THERE!

AS REPRESENTATIVE FOR THE GUACANS OF CHAU-5, I DO NOT CONDONE OR TOLERATE ANY OF THE VITRIOLIC VENOM SPEWED PREVIOUSLY. WE DO NOT, ***NEVER*** HAVE, ***NEVER*** WILL, EVER EVEN ***CONSIDER*** NOT ***EATING PEOPLE*** NEVER! ***NEVER!***
IN

WE HAVE ONE OF THE MOST EXPENSIVE, BROAD REACHING TOURISM DEPARTMENTS IN THE UNIVERSE! YOU CAN'T WALK A BLOCK WITHOUT SEEING A "COME TO CHAU-5, WE WONT EAT YOU" BILLBOARD!
VISIT CHAU-5

WHY WOULD WE PUT SO MUCH TIME AND ENERGY INTO A TOURISM DEPARTMENT IF WE WERE GOING TO ***EAT*** THE TOURISTS? ***IT DOESN'T FIT!*** AND IF IT DOESN'T FIT, YOU ***MUST AGREE WITH IT!*** SO COME TO CHAU-5 AND ***WE WONT EAT YOU!***
HELP
IN

I'M LOUISE, FROM THE TEMP AGENCY.
IF YOU'RE GOING TO BE PART OF OUR TEAM, LOUISE, YOU SHOULD MEET EVERYBODY. I'M STAN, A.K.A. **SECRET LEADER WEATHERMAN**, PILOT OF GOFOTRON'S HEAD AND BODY.

THIS IS GOFOTRON'S RIGHT AND LEFT LEGS; THE MAN ONLY KNOWN AS **SECRET SILENT SNEAKY ONE**, AND **AESOP**, A.K.A. **SECRET OPS SYSOP**.
ROOT-ROOT-RUDE-OF-ME-TO-NOT-INTRODUCE-MYSELF!

THIS IS OUR PET **SNOORF** WHO, BELIEVE IT OR NOT, IS ACTUALLY **SECRET SNOORFY SNOORFSNOORF!** BEST LEFT ARM GOFOTRON EVER HAD.
snoorf!

AND THIS IS ***LODOZE***, A.K.A. ***SECRET FLAKING NAPSTICH-NAPSTICH***. HE'S THE DARK BROODING ONE.
WHO'S THE NEW SKIRT?
I **AM** HERE FOR A TYPING POSITION, RIGHT?

HAW HAW! ***THIS*** IS SUPPOSED TA BE THE NEW RIGHT-ARM FOR GOFOTRON?
I'M **WHAT?**
JUST UNTIL SECRET ANGEL PRINCESS PRINCESS IS FOUND!

SHE'S DEADER THAN YOUR LOVE LIFE. AND WHAT A WASTE OF A NICE RACK. SEE YOU FLAKIN' NAPSTICHES LATER, I'M OFF TO THE PONYRIDES.

ON MISSIONS WE TEND TO LEAVE HIS MICROPHONE TURNED OFF.

WHAT PART OF GOFOTRON IS HE?
WE DON'T LIKE TO TALK ABOUT THAT MUCH EITHER.

READY TO TRY YOUR FIRST TRANSFORMATION, SECRET CRANKY OFFICE TEMP?

I DON'T LIKE MY CODENAME! I'M NOT CRANKY!
THAT'S WHAT MAKES IT SUCH A SECRET CODENAME! LIKE ALL OF OURS! NOW HOLD YOUR GOFOWRIST-THINGY UP AND SAY THE MAGIC WORDS.

GO-GO...

...GOFOEEEEK!

I WAS NAKED!
YES!

I MEAN, THE MOLECULES OF YOUR UNIFORM GO TRANSPARENT BEFORE REPIGMENTATION FOR CALIBRATION STUFF THINGIES.

BUT DON'T YOU GUYS GET EMBARRASSED WHEN IT HAPPENS TO YOU?
huh?

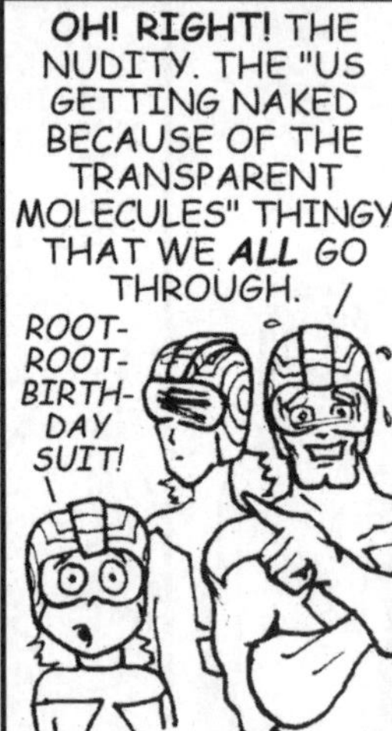
OH! RIGHT! THE NUDITY. THE "US GETTING NAKED BECAUSE OF THE TRANSPARENT MOLECULES" THINGY THAT WE ALL GO THROUGH.
ROOT-ROOT-BIRTH-DAY SUIT!

ONLY THE WOMEN'S OUTFITS GO TRANSPARENT, RIGHT?
LOOKS LIKE SOMEBODY'S CRANKY!

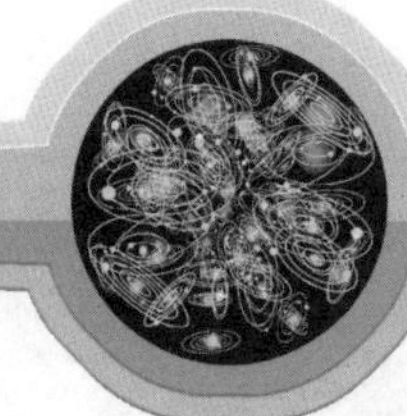

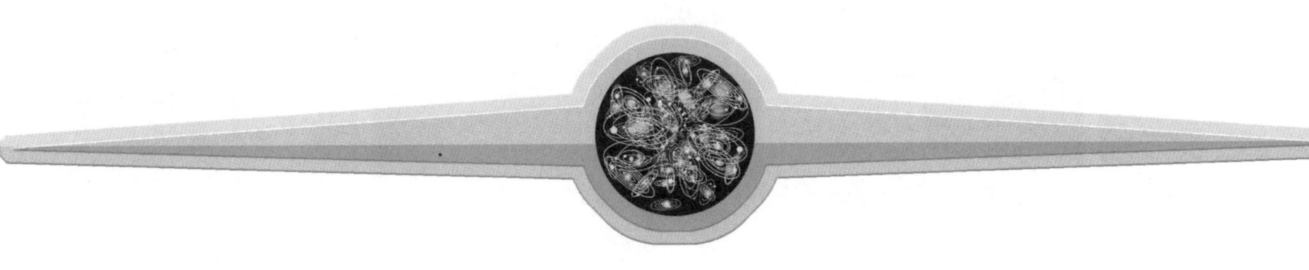

SCANDAL ROCKS THE LOHVO ARMY AS INVESTIGATORS LEARN THAT GENERAL BENEDICT IS BEHIND THE THEFT OF THE CASCADE MISSILE! DOES OUR GREATEST GENERAL WORK FOR THE ZORGONS? HE'S BARRICADED HIMSELF IN HIS MILITARY BASE AT HUT-2. WE HAVE LIVE FOOTAGE OF HIM HOLDING SOME KIND OF PACKAGE...

MEANWHILE, AT BASE GOFOTRON...
IT'S ONE OF GOLA'S "SPECIAL" PACKAGES! SNOORF!
GOLA'S GOING TO IMBUE HIM! WE'VE GOT TO GET THERE FAST!
IMBUE HIM?

ZORGON GOLA CAN CREATE MONSTERS AND IMBUE THEM WITH SPECIAL POWERS! ON GRITTANIA 3 HE TURNED A VEGETABLE INTO A MONSTER AND IMBUED IT WITH IRON SKIN!

AND ONCE HE IMBUED A COW-MONSTER WITH BARBECUE SAUCE!
M-m-m-m-m!

MEANWHILE ON HUT-2...

GOLA PROMISES ME A WEAPON AGAINST GOFOTRON, AND HE SENDS ME A SIX-PACK OF BLARG?

MEANWHILE-MEANWHILE ON RHIBB PRIME...
YOU WERE PROMISED THE WEAPON TO DEFEAT GOFOTRON AND IT IS YOU!

MEANWHILE-WHILE-WHILE, IN SPACE...
THE MONSTER RAY LEAVES RHIBB PRIME AND STREAKS ACROSS THE PUNYVERSE.

BACK TO HUT-2...
STRIKING GENERAL BENEDICT, IT TRANSFORMS HIM INTO A MONSTER IMBUED WITH THE BLARG NEARBY.

HE IS GENERAL BENEDICT NO MORE! NOW HE IS...
KEGS BENEDICT
PAR-TAY

OUCH. THAT HURT. AND BACK AGAIN TO BASE GOFOTRON.

IF ZORGON GOLA CAN TURN ANYONE OR ANYTHING INTO MONSTERS THAT SERVE HIM, WHY DOESN'T HE JUST TURN US ALL INTO MONSTERS AND WIN THE WAR IN ONE FELL...

Umph

SHHHH! JEEZ, DO YOU WANT TO JUST **HAND** THE KEYS OF THE UNIVERSE OVER TO HIM?

YES, KEGS BENEDICT IS FEELING NO PAIN, BEING IMBUED WITH THE SPACE BOOZE KNOWN AS BLARG! HIS CONFIDENCE IS SKYROCKETING, HIS ADRENALINE IS PUMPING, AND HE'S ALMOST INVINCIBLE! THERE ARE, HOWEVER, DISADVANTAGES TO BLARG. WE REJOIN THIS COMBAT ALREADY IN PROGRESS.

YOU FORGET, GOFOTRON NEVER LOSES. WE'LL STOP ZORGON GOLA FROM USING CASCADE MISSILES TO BLOW UP PLANETS!

YAWN! HE'S NOT GOING TO DESHTROY SOME PLANETSHHH, HE'SH GOING TO DESHTROY THE WHOLE UNIVERSE WITH ONE MISHILE...

IT'S ANOTHER VICTORY FOR GOFOTRON, WHOSE LAST DEED WAS TO MAKE SURE THE ZORGON MONSTER GOT A TAXI HOME INSTEAD OF GETTING BEHIND THE WHEEL! REMEMBER, FRIENDS DON'T LET FRIENDS BLARG-FACE THROUGH SPACE!

THE CASCADE MISSILE DELIVERS AN ENERGY SIGNATURE THAT DESTABILIZES ENERGY SYSTEMS ON A HUGE SCALE. SAY, FOR EXAMPLE, THE MOLTEN CORE OF A PLANET, OR A SMALL PUPPY. WHEN FIRED INTO A SUN, IT TRIGGERS A SUPERNOVA OF THAT SUN, SENDING THE ENERGY SIGNATURE IN ALL DIRECTIONS, INFECTING OTHER SUNS, CREATING A CASCADE EFFECT OF SUPERNOVAS. BENEDICT WAS RIGHT. A SINGLE CASCADE MISSILE LAUNCHED INTO **ANY** SUN WILL **COMPLETELY** DESTROY THE **ENTIRE** UNIVERSE.

BUT KING PROAN, EVEN A MAN AS INSANELY EVIL AS **ZORGON GOLA** WOULDN'T BE FOOLISH ENOUGH TO DESTROY HIMSELF AND EVERYTHING ELSE IN THE UNIVERSE.... WOULD HE?

PREPARE TO LAUNCH A CASCADE MISSILE AT MY COMMAND!
WHAT IS OUR TARGET, LORD GOLA?
A SMALL PUPPY.

NO, SECRET CRANKY OFFICE TEMP, WE MUST ASSUME HE IS EVEN MORE FOOLISHLY INSANE AND EVILLY... FOOLISH.

MEANWHILE, ON CHAU 5...
OUCHY!
AK.

THOSE WERE THE ONLY GUACANS STILL ON US, SO I THINK WE'RE SAFE!
I THOUGHT YOU **KNEW** THESE GUYS!

THE GUACANS HAVE BEEN WORKING FOR THE ZORGONS FOR CENTURIES. I HAD NO IDEA THEY WOULD TURN ON US WHEN WE ASKED FOR HELP. DID THE OTHERS GET AWAY?
THEIR "TENDERIZER RAY" GOT THEM ALL. EVEN BUN-BUN. I'D HATE TO BE THEM WHEN THE RAY WEARS OFF!

WHAT ARE THEY GOING TO DO WITH HIM?
THEY DON'T EAT RABBITS. THEY PREFER HUMANOIDS.
OH, RIGHT. THEY'RE GOING TO EAT HIM FIRST. I FORGOT.

IS YOU MY PET BUNNY-WUNNY? YES YOU ARE!
ZAPPED, STUNNED, RIBS CRACKED, BONES BROKEN, AND NOW, I'M IMMOBILIZED AND HUMILIATED. I HATE THIS FREAKIN' PUNYVERSE!
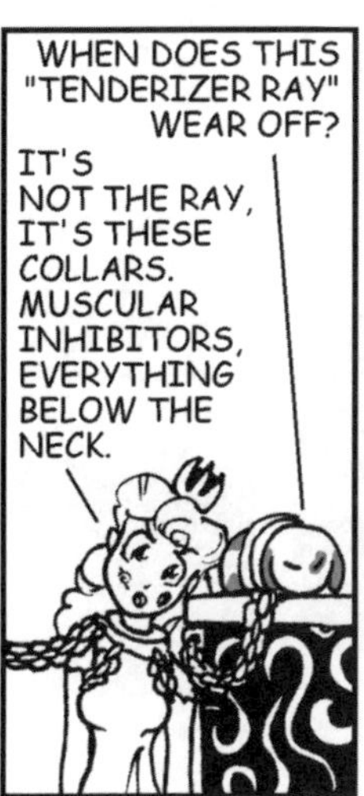
WHEN DOES THIS "TENDERIZER RAY" WEAR OFF?
IT'S NOT THE RAY, IT'S THESE COLLARS. MUSCULAR INHIBITORS, EVERYTHING BELOW THE NECK.

WHAT HAPPENED TO RIFF?
THEY MADE HIM A FROZEN DESSERT FOR TONIGHT
WHY AREN'T YOU DINNER?

THEY RECOGNIZED ME AS THE LOHVO PRINCESS. WANT TO AUCTION ME OFF... eep!
RIGHT. BUT THERE'S NO REASON WE CAN'T SLICE OFF A CHUNK OR TWO FOR SNACKS, S'LONG AS YOU SURVIVE IT! *MUAHAHAHA!*
YANK!

NOT THAT WE EAT PEOPLE OR ANYTHING.
HEY, MAN, IT'S YOUR BAG.

I STILL SAY "HEAVY BLUNT OBJECT" LIKE THIS ROCK!
AND I SAY WE RELY ON MY MIND-CONTROL ABILITY!
SECURITY STATION 01

YOU WILL LIE DOWN AND TAKE A NAP!
HUH?
ITY

WHAM!

I WILL LIE DOWN AND TAKE A NAP.

LET'S JUST CALL THAT TEAMWORK.
CALL THAT TEAMWORK...
Z Z Z Z Z Z

HE WAS STILL LOGGED IN! WE HAVE FULL ACCESS... THIS LOOKS **BAD!** THEY'RE TAKING THE PRINCESS TO THE KITCHEN. THEY'RE GOING TO RANSOM HER OFF, BUT THEY'RE GOING TO COOK AT LEAST PART OF HER FOR TONIGHT'S DINNER PARTY! AND **RIFF'S THE DESSERT!**

HERE'S THE COMM-THINGY. WHO DO WE CALL FOR HELP? THE LOHVOS OR THE ZORGONS? I MEAN, HANDING PRINCESS-PRINCESS OVER TO YOUR LEADER MEANS A LOT TO YOU, BUT THIS IS LOHVO SPACE AND...
CALL THE LOHVOS. I'M GOING TO GO SAVE THE PRINCESS.
SECURITY STATION 01

WHAT ABOUT SECURITY?
TURNED IT OFF. TALK ABOUT EGGS IN ONE BASKET, I ONLY HAD TO HIT ONE SWITCH TO DO IT!
AND THAT TOOK CARE OF **ALL** THE SECURITY MEASURES?
worn

POP!
YOUR COLLAR FELL OFF, BUNNY-WUNNY! I'LL GET YOU A NEW ONE, AND A NEW BOW! YOU'LL LIKE THAT!

FIRST LET ME CORRECT YOU ON HOW TO PROPERLY TIE THE KNOT IN THE BOW.

I'M THINKING A PRINCESS-PRINCESS RIGHT-ARM PIZZA-PIZZA. SOUND GOOD TO YOU?

MIND IF I CUT IN?
worn
worn

CHOP
YEARGH!!
OOPS.

GRATER HAS THE PRINCESS, LET ME SEE IF I CAN SAVE RIFF. BUN-BUN CAN TAKE CARE OF HIMSELF.

AND EVERYBODY ELSE, FROM THE LOOKS OF IT.
WHAT TOOK YOU SO LONG, NERD-BOY?
I WAS GOING TO ASK YOU THE SAME THING!

WE'VE GOT TO GET RIFF OUT OF THIS. I HOPE HE'S STILL ALIVE!

LATER, AFTER TORG AND GRATER REGROUP...
LOOKS LIKE BUN-BUN PRETTY MUCH CLEANED THE GUACANS OUT OF THIS PALACE. THAT BOIL-IN-A-BAG LOOKS LIKE A PAINFUL WAY TO DEFROST RIFF. HEY, DOES THAT BAG HAVE AIR HOLES?

ZAP
ZAP
ZAP
Poing

OH GREAT. NOW HE'S DROWNING.
DOES NOW.

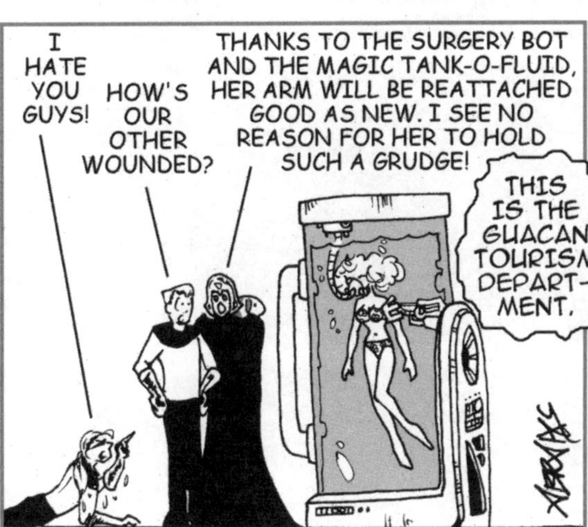
I HATE YOU GUYS!
HOW'S OUR OTHER WOUNDED?
THANKS TO THE SURGERY BOT AND THE MAGIC TANK-O-FLUID, HER ARM WILL BE REATTACHED GOOD AS NEW. I SEE NO REASON FOR HER TO HOLD SUCH A GRUDGE!

THIS IS THE GUACAN TOURISM DEPARTMENT.
PLEASE COME OUT, GARNISHED, WITH YOUR HANDS UP, SO THAT WE CAN PROCESS YOU. I MEAN YOUR PASSPORTS, SO YOU CAN GET BACK TO ENJOYING YOUR VACATION!

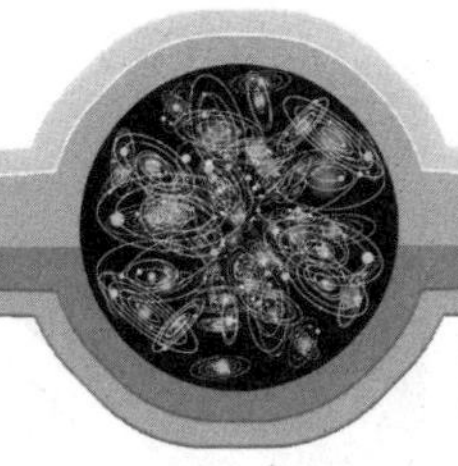

HUH? WHAT'S GOING ON?
RELAX. YOU'RE GROGGY AND...
GET YOUR HANDS OFF ME!

I JUST SAVED YOUR LIFE. HOW ABOUT A KISS?
NOT IF YOU WERE THE LAST MAN IN THE UNIVERSE!
KEEP IT DOWN, KIDS. THE GUACAN TOURISM DEPARTMENT HAS THIS BUILDING SURROUNDED. WE NEED TO FIGURE OUT A WAY TO ESCAPE.

I DON'T THINK WE NEED TO WORRY ABOUT THAT.

MY DISTRESS CALL GOT THROUGH.
GO-GO-GOFOTRON.

FOR HIS HELP IN MY DAUGHTER'S RESCUE, LORD GRATER'S LIFE SHALL BE SPARED. BUT HER OTHER RESCUERS SHALL BE HONORED. SEND ONE HUNDRED OF MY FINEST OFFICERS TO JOIN GOFOTRON ON CHAU.

Sluggy Freelance

CLAP CLAP CLAP CLAP CLAP CLAP CLAP CLAP
CLAP CLAP CLAP CLAP CLAP CLAP CLAP

IT IS A GREAT HONOR FOR ME TO BESTOW THE MEDAL OF NEAT-O TO YOU WHO HAVE SAVED MY DAUGHTER.

WE TOO OF TEAM GOFOTRON WOULD LIKE TO OFFER OUR COMMENDATION BLA-BLA BLA BLA
HUH?

BLA BLA MY LEADERSHIP BLA BLA BLA CHIN LIKE MINE BLA BLA BLA BLA...
YOU!
YOU!

DIE, YOU FLAKIN' NAPSTICHES!
RUN FOR YOUR LIVES! EEEY-AAAAH!
THE GUACANS ARE ATTACKING!

YAMA
WE'RE REPORTING LIVE FROM CHAU 5 WHERE CHAOS HAS BROKEN OUT! IT APPEARS TO BE A FREE-FOR-ALL INVOLVING KING PROAN'S TROOPS, ZORGON SPIES, TEAM GOFOTRON, AND A HORDE OF RAMPAGING GUACANS. AND IN THE MIDDLE OF IT ALL, MUCH TO THE UNIVERSE'S RELIEF, SECRET ANGEL PRINCESS-PRINCESS HAS RETURNED TO PROTECT THE INNOCENT! FOR REACTION, WE GO TO VACADO, HEAD OF THE GUACAN TOURISM DEPARTMENT.

YAMA, THIS IS SIMPLY OFF-WORLD VIOLENCE BROUGHT TO OUR PEACEFUL PLANET. WHY, I LOOK AT THIS FOOTAGE AND SEE NOBLE GUACANS PROTECTING THEIR HOMELAND WITH AXE AND STEEL! AND... UM .. SALT AND PEPPER.
OK, SO WE ACCIDENTALLY SLOW ROAST AND EAT PEOPLE IN SELF-DEFENSE! BUT YOU ANTI-GUACANS MAKE LIKE IT'S COMMON PRACTICE IN YOUR GUACAN WITCH-HUNT. ***A FEW MINOR INCIDENTS FROM A FEW INNOCENT GUACANS, AND NEXT THING YOU KNOW YOU WANT TO BOIL US ALL IN ONE BIG POT!***
VACADO THE GUACAN

CALL CULINARY AND TELL THEM TO ORDER ONE BIG POT, I JUST HAD A GREAT IDEA!

ZOOM!

WHICHEVER ONE OF YOU GUYS HAS THE REMOTE, HOP IN. WE'RE BEE-LINING TO THE GRITTANIA SYSTEM AND GOING HOME. I'M SICK OF THIS PLACE!

WHERE'D YOU GET THE SHIP?
JUST HOT-WIRED ONE.
WITH A LITTLE HELP FROM A FRIEND!

I'M SO GLAD YOU'RE BACK, SECRET ANGEL PRINCESS-PRINCESS! IT WON'T BE ME STUCK WITH YOUR WEIRD TEAMMATES ANYMORE!

WAIT FOR ME!

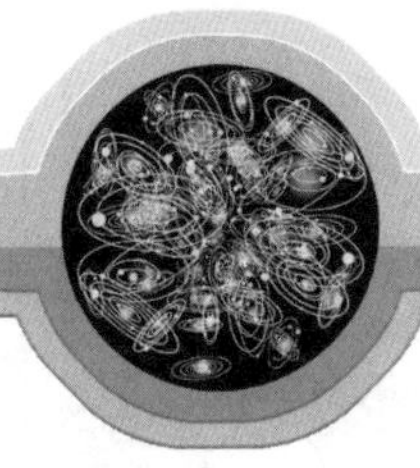

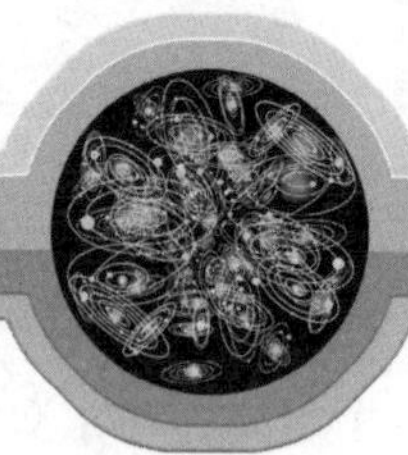

THE FOLLOWING ARMAGEDDON ANNOUNCEMENT IS BROUGHT TO YOU BY STEPH'S BLARG.

ATTENTION TO ALL OF YOU ABOUT TO DIE AS OUR UNIVERSE GOES SUPERNOVA: I, ZORGON GOLA, HAVE CREATED A MONSTER FROM A PUPPY
STEPH'S BLARG

STOP YOUR LAUGHING! THIS IS NO ORDINARY PUPPY!

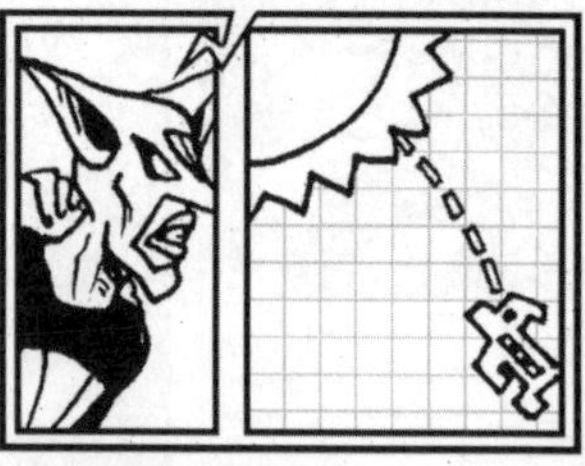

A PUPPY TRANSPLANTED WITH THE MIND OF A MOTH AND IMBUED WITH A CASCADE MISSILE, IT IS, AS WE SPEAK, DOGGY-PADDLING STRAIGHT FOR A SUN IN AN OUT-WORLD SYSTEM! I CALL HIM... SCOOTER!

SCOOTER WILL TRIGGER DOOMSDAY, MY DEAR GOFOTRON, AND THERE IS NOTHING YOU CAN DO ABOUT IT. YOU WILL NEVER GET THERE IN TIME.

YES WE WILL, GOLA. WITH THE SPEED OF OUR AMAZINGLY HASTY DRIVE.

FOR-FOR-FORM GO-GO-GOFOTRON!

WITH LIGHTNING SPEED, THE SIX SHIPS OF GOFOTRON PREPARE TO UNITE!
NO FAIR! SECRET ANGEL IS BACK! I QUIT! I WANT OUT!

RIFF? WHAT JUST HAPPENED?
WE CHANGED COURSE. WE'RE TURNING AWAY FROM GRITTANIA, HEADING BACK TOWARDS CHAU! IT'S FLYING ON AUTOMATIC!
REMOTE AUTO-PILOT

MOMENTS LATER:
WHERE'S SECRET FLAKING NAP-STICH-NAPSTICH? HIS SHIP SHOULD BE HERE BY NOW!
CLANK! CLANK! CLANK!
EVERYTHING HAS A MANUAL.
WE'RE BACK IN CONTROL!

SIR, SOME OF THE TROOPS ARE CONCERNED ABOUT SCOOTER REACHING THE SUN AND DESTROYING THE UNIVERSE. Y'KNOW, THE "KILLING ALL OF US" PART.

I KNOW. I KNOW ABOUT THE SIX SHIPS THAT MAKE TEAM GOFOTRON. I KNOW ABOUT THEIR AMAZINGLY HASTY DRIVE. I KNOW THEY THINK I'M CRAZY ENOUGH TO DESTROY THE UNIVERSE. THAT IS WHY MY PLAN IS **PURELY PERFECT!**

HA-HA-HA

GOFOTRON WILL DEFEAT SCOOTER, BUT DETONATING THE CASCADE-PUPPY WILL DESTROY GOFOTRON AT BEST, SEVERELY INJURE HIM AT WORST. HISTORY HAS SHOWN THIS.

AND HERE WE ARE, MY ENTIRE ARMY, CLOAKED AROUND EVERY MAJOR WORLD IN LOHVO TERRITORY, WAITING FOR GOFOTRON'S FIGHT TO BEGIN. THEN WE SHALL UNLEASH OUR FURY ON THOSE WHO DO NOT SURRENDER. BETWEEN THEIR ARMY'S WEAKNESS, GOFOTRON'S INJURIES, AND RUMORS OF OUR ALLIANCE WITH THE VOID-GHOSTS, VICTORY IS ASSURED!

BUT SIR, GOFOTRON HAS TO **FORM** TO FIGHT, AND ITS GROIN JUST FLEW THAT-A-WAY! ACCORDING TO ZORGON SKULL-CHIP TRACKING, **LORD GRATER** IS ON BOARD.

NOOOOOO!
NO...NO... UNCLOAK US NOW AND **AFTER THAT SHIP!**

NOW NOTHING IS STANDING BETWEEN US AND GRITTANIA.
EXCEPT FOR THAT BIG ZORGON DEATH SHIP THAT JUST APPEARED OUT OF NOWHERE.

WHAT DO YOU THINK OF MY CHANCES TO HOOK UP WITH PRINCESS-PRINCESS?
I'M A LITTLE MORE CON-CERNED ABOUT THAT "DEATH-SHIP" RIGHT NOW!
WEAPONS LOCKING ON.

ALL RIGHT. CHOPPING OFF HER ARM WAS BAD, AND KNOCKING HER OUT WITH THE LANDING GEAR WASN'T A PLUS EITHER.
WHAT ABOUT ME TYING HER UP? KINKY, HUH?
OH, COME ON!

YOU WEREN'T BEING KINKY. YOU'RE AFRAID SHE'S GOING TO HURT YOU WHEN SHE WAKES UP.
NAH. I WAS JUST TALKIN' CRAZY THEN.
WHAT THE HELL IS GOING ON HERE?

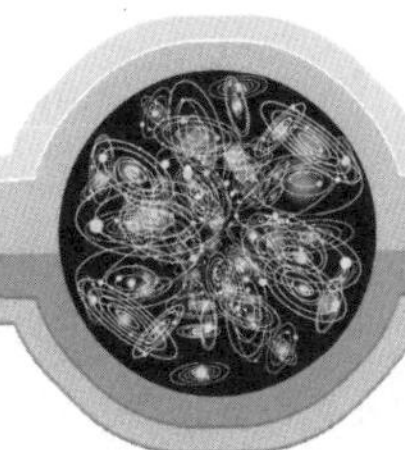

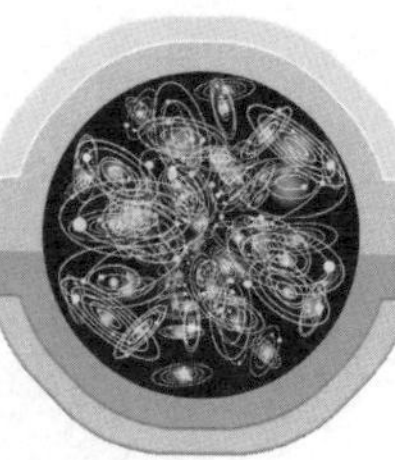

THE WAY THAT SHIP CAME OUT OF NOWHERE... YOU ZORGONS **DO** HAVE VOID-GHOST TECHNOLOGY!
VOID GHOSTS ARE A MYTH. WE DEVELOPED CLOAKING ON OUR OWN.
WHAT'S A VOID GHOST?

I READ ABOUT THIS WHEN WE WERE ON GRITTANIA. THERE IS A BELIEF THAT THE VOID SURROUNDING THIS UNIVERSE IS FULL OF INVISIBLE ALIENS WHO ATTACK THOSE INVADING THEIR TERRITORY.
VOID
UNIVERSE

NO ONE HAS EVER CAPTURED EVIDENCE OF THESE "VOID GHOSTS".
YES, BECAUSE NO SHIP EXPLORING THE VOID TOO FAR IN ANY DIRECTION HAS EVER RETURNED. NO TRACE, NO NOTHING.

AND THE REASON WHY THE OUTWORLD SYSTEMS ARE ONLY GOOD FOR MINING IS FROM RANDOM ENERGY-BEAM BOMBARDMENTS FROM THE VOID. KILLS THE SOUL OF THE PLANET, SOME SAY.
THAT WOULD EXPLAIN WHY THERE'S LIFE EVERYWHERE IN THIS LITTLE-BALL UNIVERSE EXCEPT ON THE OUTSIDE OF THE BALL.
GOFOTRON WON'T EVEN VENTURE OUT THERE!

VORTBOOM

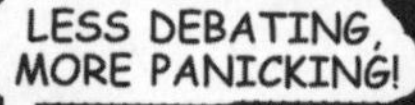
LESS DEBATING, MORE PANICKING!

THIS SHIP IS SURPRISINGLY SLOW FOR ITS SIZE. WE CAN'T OUT-RUN GOLA'S DEATH-SHIP.
LET'S HIDE IN THAT ASTEROID BELT.

I VOTE WE GO PLANETSIDE, ABANDON THIS SHIP, AND HIDE OUT!
ACCORDING TO THE COMPUTERS, THE ONLY INHABITABLE PLANET NEARBY IS BARAS 9.

BARAS 9. "PLANET OF THE NAKED NYMPHO-MANIACS".

ATTENTION BARAS 9, WE NEED TO MAKE AN EMERGENCY LANDING!

PLEASE COME IN, BARAS 9! WE NEED TO MAKE AN EMERGENCY LANDING. IT HAS NOTHING TO DO WITH THE FACT THAT YOU ARE KNOWN AS THE PLANET OF NAKED NYMPHO-MANIACS!

HI GUYS! COME ON DOWN! GOT ANY FEMALES? WE'RE FRESH OUT OF 'EM.

EEEEK!
LET'S SURRENDER TO GOLA.
RUN AWAY!
TEE-HEE
I'LL SAVE YOU, PRINCESS-PRINCESS!
BEEP

WHOOAAAAAH!

HEADING FOR THE VOID! STOP!
CAN'T STOP!

WARP BUTTON STUCK! GOT SOMETHING TO PRY IT UP WITH?
PAPER-CLIPS!

WE'RE ALL GONNA DIE!
PRY!

THEY ESCAPED?
THEY BLEW OUR DOORS OFF, SIR. AMAZINGLY HASTY DRIVE.
IT'S TIME TO UNLEASH OUR HORRIBLY UNTESTED "WE'RE ALL GONNA DIE" DRIVE! AFTER THEM!

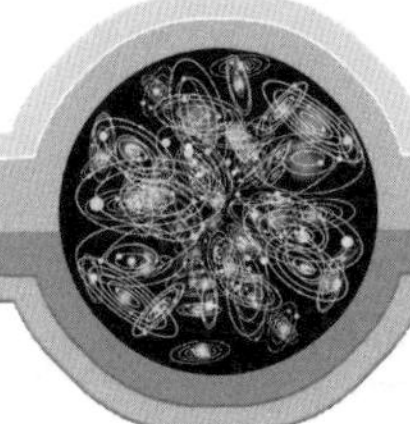

CLICK!
WRRRRRRRRRR

WE'RE OUT IN THE VOID. THIS IS A DANGEROUS PLACE.
THAT WAS THE AMAZINGLY HASTY DRIVE! WE'RE PILOTING A PART OF GOFOTRON?

OF COURSE. FROM ALL THE SPACE-PORN ON THE FLOOR, I SHOULD HAVE KNOWN I WAS IN LODOZE'S SHIP.
SPACE PORN!?!
SLUGGY FREELANCE

MEANWHILE, IN A DISTANT OUTWORLD SYSTEM, SCOOTER THE WONDER DOG OF DOOM HEADS TOWARDS THE SUN.
OH BOY, OH BOY! I'M GONNA GET IT. GONNA GET DA SUN. OH BOY, OH BOY, OH BOY!

MEANWHILE-MEANWHILE, KING LOHVO PROAN MAKES A DESPERATE PLEA TO GOFOTRON...
GOFOTRON, YOU HAVE TO STOP SCOOTER THE CASCADE-PUPPY OF DOOM OR THE UNIVERSE WILL BE DESTROYED!

WELL, YOUR MAJESTY, GOFOTRON IS ONLY PARTLY FORMED, HE'S MISSING HIS, UM, HIS MOTIVATION.

WELL, SEPARATE AND SHOOT THAT PUPPY DOWN FROM YOUR HASTY SHIPS!
TAK TAK TAK
GOFOTRON DOESN'T SEEM TO CARE TO SEPARATE. OR DO ANY-THING. GOFOTRON WON'T BUDGE. IT'S LIKE HE HAS NO-THING TO LIVE FOR.

WELL TEAM, IT LOOKS LIKE WE'RE ABOUT TO GET OUR BUTTS KICKED.
SNORF IT ALL TO SNORF.
WHO CAREZ?
WHERE COULD LODOZE BE?
ROOT-ROOT-RUDY GIULIANI!

CAUSE OF DEATH, DETECTIVE?
BACK OF HIS HEAD GOT HOLLOWED OUT BY A LIGHTSABER.
CASE CLOSED, LET'S EAT.
OIM NAUT DED YET!

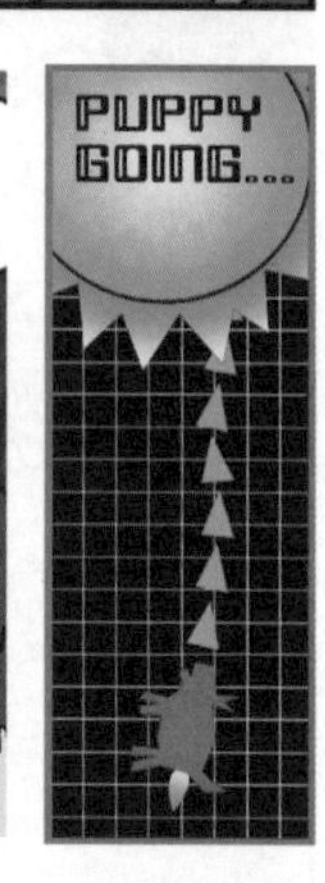
PUPPY GOING...

SO, THIS IS HOW IT ALL ENDS. I MUST CONFESS, I THOUGHT IT MIGHT BE GOLA'S INSANITY THAT DESTROYED US ALL.

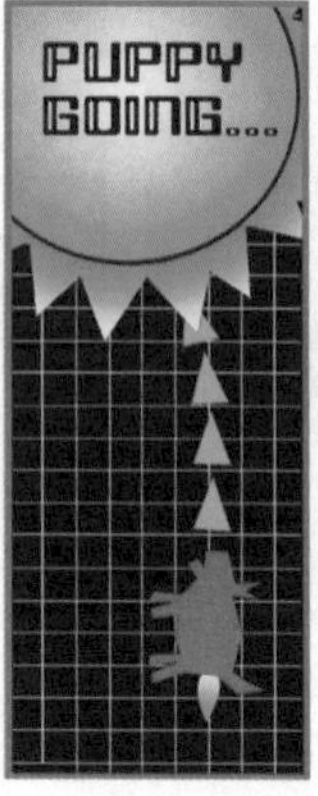
PUPPY GOING...

SINCE WE'RE DOING CONFESSIONS, I MAY AS WELL FESS UP. THIS WHOLE GOFOTRON THING WAS AN EXCUSE TO SEE YOUR DAUGHTER NAKED.
WHAT?!?

PUPPY GOING...

SEE, ONLY THE WOMEN'S TEAM OUTFITS TURN TRANSPARENT. IT STARTED AS A DARE, REALLY. THEN WE DID A MISSION OR TWO, AND BEFORE YOU KNOW IT, HERE WE ARE!
YOU MEAN MY PRINCESS-PRINCESS IS SECRET ANGEL PRINCESS-PRINCESS? BOY THAT SOUNDED STUPID WHEN I SAID IT OUT LOUD.

PUPPY GONE.
PLOOP

OK, YOU IDIOTS. I'M TAKING OVER. I WANT YOU TO TELL ME EXACTLY WHAT'S GOING ON WITH GOLA, WITH LODOZE, AND WITH GOFOTRON.
WELL, FOR STARTERS, THERE'S THAT.
PLAYBOT

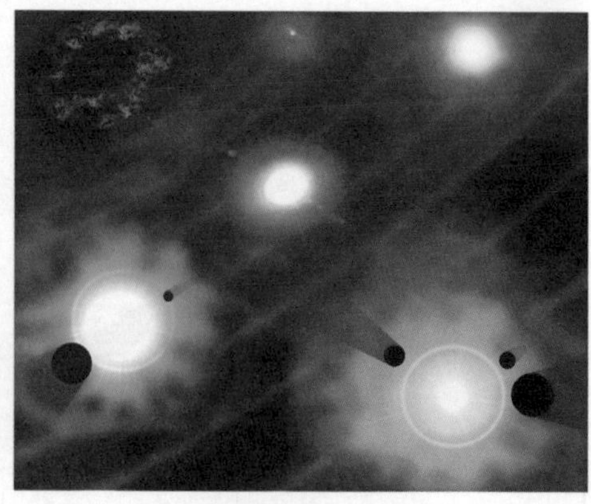

EVERYTHING BLEW UP? **EVERYBODY IS *DEAD?***
I DON'T KNOW WHAT HAPPENED, BUT HANG ON! HERE COMES THE SHOCKWAVE!

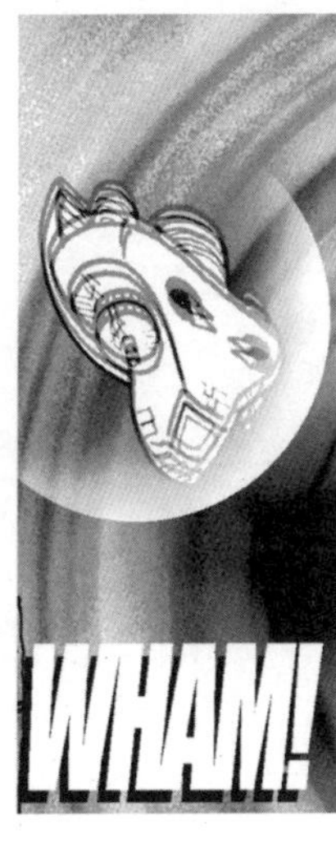
WHAM!

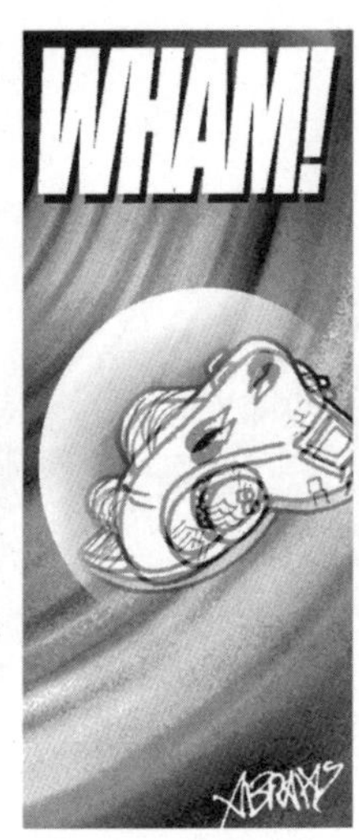
WHAM!

A WAVE FROM THE OTHER DIRECTION HIT US TOO? **WHAT THE HELL IS GOING ON?**
A SIGNAL! GOLA'S DEATH-SHIP, COMING AT US FAST!

LOOK OUT!

CONGRATULATIONS, ZORGON GOLA! THE TEST OF THE "WE'RE ALL GOING TO DIE" DRIVE PROVES IT IS EVEN FASTER THAN THAT HASTY DRIVE! ANOTHER TRIUMPH OF ZORGON SCIENCE.
WE'RE GOING TOO FAR INTO THE VOID. HIT THE BRAKES!

WELL, WE DON'T ACTUALLY *HAVE* BRAKES FOR THE DRIVE YET.
WHAT?
WELL, DON'T WORRY, THAT'S WHY WE DO TEST RUNS SUCH AS THIS. I'M TAKING VERY GOOD NOTES!
WE'RE ALL GOING TO

POOF!

ZAP!

WE'RE HIT! THAT RAY PUNCHED RIGHT THROUGH OUR SHIELDS!
THE VOID GHOSTS ARE ATTACKING!

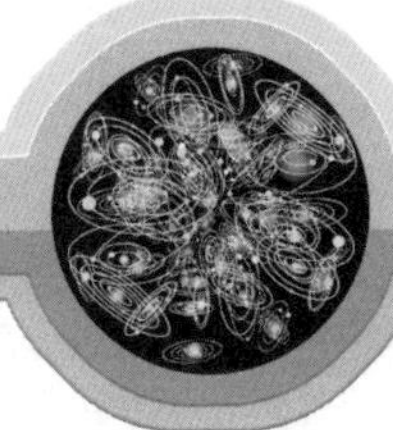

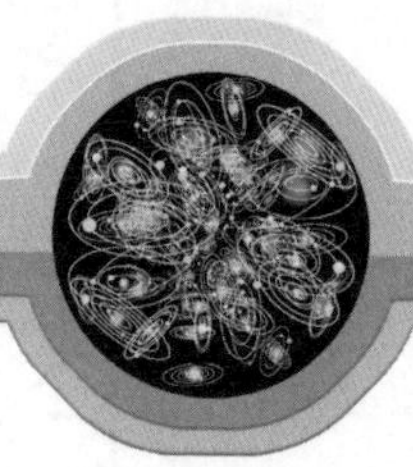

THERE ARE NO VOID GHOSTS, PRINCESS. WE ZORGONS PERPETUATED THE RUMORS FOR OUR OWN ENDS. RIFF, IF YOU WILL CHECK THE LONG-RANGE SCAN RECORDS, YOU WILL SEE GOLA'S SHIP ACTUALLY HIT ... ***THE EDGE OF THE UNIVERSE.***

IT'S WHY THAT SHOCKWAVE BOUNCED BACK AT US BEFORE. THE EDGE REFLECTS EVERYTHING BACK AS ENERGY. WHEN GOLA'S SHIP HIT THAT EDGE ... **POOF. ZAP.** THAT SIMPLE.

WE'RE IN A FISHBOWL! THAT'S WHY THIS UNIVERSE IS SO SMALL! NO ROOM TO GROW! ANY ROCK OR SHIP GOING BEYOND A CERTAIN POINT IS CONVERTED TO ENERGY AND REBOUNDED BACK AT THE SPEED OF LIGHT! RANDOM DEBRIS IN SPACE WOULD BE ENOUGH TO CHAR THE OUTWORLD SYSTEMS OVER A MILLENNIUM!
SPEAKING OF DEBRIS, I THINK I'M LOOKING AT A SPHERICAL WAVE OF DEBRIS **EXPANDING OUR WAY!**
ALL THE MATTER IN THE UNIVERSE! IT'S BUILDING UP AS IT GOES!

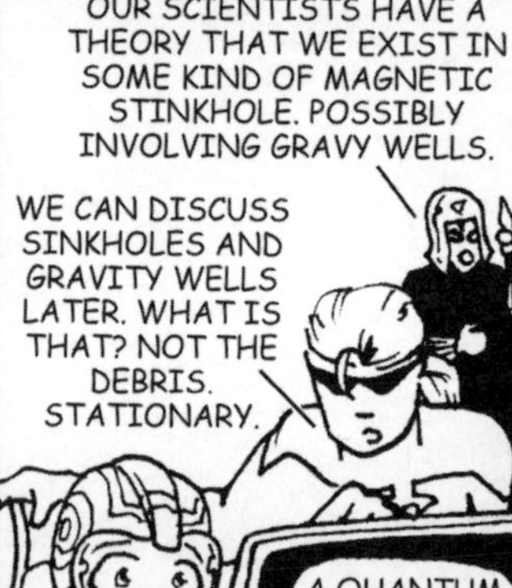

OUR SCIENTISTS HAVE A THEORY THAT WE EXIST IN SOME KIND OF MAGNETIC STINKHOLE. POSSIBLY INVOLVING GRAVY WELLS.
WE CAN DISCUSS SINKHOLES AND GRAVITY WELLS LATER. WHAT IS THAT? NOT THE DEBRIS. STATIONARY.
A QUANTUM SINGULARITY. IN THE VERY CENTER OF THE UNIVERSE.

DAMN! KNOWING WHERE THE CENTER OF THE UNIVERSE IS DOESN'T HELP ME AT ALL. WE CAN PUNCH THROUGH THE DEBRIS COMING, BUT WHEN IT HITS THE EDGE OF THE VOID AND BOUNCES BACK AS ENERGY, WE'RE TOAST.

THIS SHIP'S ENGINES ARE GONE. THAT LEAVES THE SHUTTLE-POD, WHICH CAN ONLY HOLD TWO. THAT MEANS ME, AND RIFF TO WORK THE REMOTE. SO SEE THE REST OF YOU GUYS LATER.
KA CLICK

IT'S GOT ROOM FOR TWO "US"-SIZED PEOPLE, BUN-BUN. I'M SURE YOU CAN FIT ANOTHER. PRINCESS-PRINCESS SHOULD GO.
FINE. 'SLONG AS I CAN STUFF HER IN THE GLOVE COMPARTMENT.
IT DOESN'T MATTER, BUN-BUN. WE CAN'T FIND OUR WAY HOME. THERE IS NOTHING OUT THERE LEFT TO NAVIGATE BY. I HAVE NO IDEA WHERE THE PORTAL WILL OPEN.

I DON'T KNOW WHAT TO DO.

WAIT A MINUTE. IF THERE'S NOTHING OUT THERE, AND WE OPEN THE PORTAL, WON'T IT BE EASY TO SPOT ON THE SCANNERS?
ASSUMING IT'S IN SCANNING RANGE... THAT'S A GREAT IDEA! LET'S TRY IT!

BEEP
WOW! IT WORKED! GOT IT!

YES!

YOU DON'T THINK THE GIRLS WERE WAITING ON THE OTHER SIDE OF THE PORTAL WHEN WE OPENED IT UP TO THE VACUUM OF SPACE, DO YOU?
MAYBE I SHOULD CLOSE IT.

WHOAH!!

THE REPORT I SPENT ALL LAST WEEK ON JUST GOT SUCKED INTO SPACE; I AM SO GOING TO KILL THEM IF THEY MAKE IT HOME.

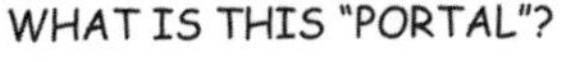

WHAT IS THIS "PORTAL"?
LONG-STORY-SHORT: WE'RE FROM SOMEPLACE ELSE, AND WE CAN OPEN A DOOR-WAY TO SAFETY BEFORE THE UNIVERSE BLOWS UP AGAIN. AT LEAST BUN-BUN AND TWO OF US CAN ESCAPE.

WAIT! I HAVE ANOTHER IDEA! WE PUT THE SHUTTLE-POD ON EXTREMELY PRECISE AUTOPILOT. THEN WE ALL RIDE PIGGYBACK ON IT LIKE A WAVE-RUNNER AND DIVE THROUGH THE PORTAL AT THE LAST POSSIBLE MOMENT!

LET'S DO IT.
YOU GUYS ARE DEFINITELY FROM SOMEPLACE ELSE.
I'M RIDING ON THE INSIDE OF THE POD. ALL NERD-BOYS CAN DO WHAT THEY WANT.

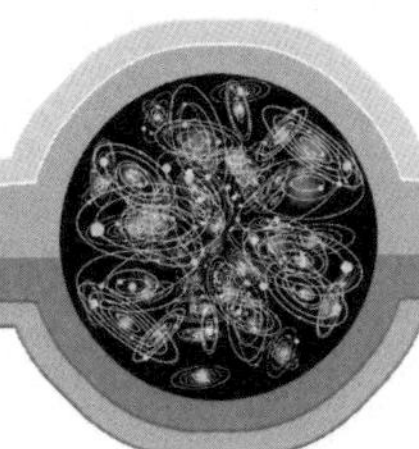

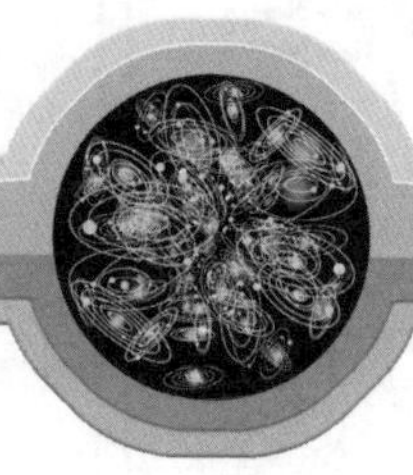

WE PUNCHED THROUGH THE DEBRIS. YOU AND PRINCESS-PRINCESS BETTER SUIT UP. COMING WITH US IS THE ONLY WAY YOU'RE GOING TO LIVE.
WE'VE DECIDED TO STAY.

WHAT?
THIS IS OUR HOME. WE DON'T BELONG IN YOUR UNIVERSE. WE'LL BE HAPPIER HERE.

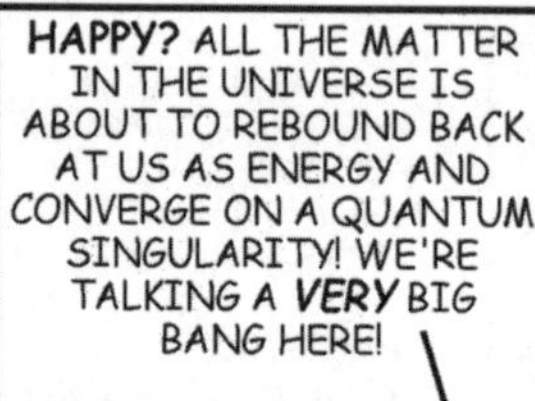

HAPPY? ALL THE MATTER IN THE UNIVERSE IS ABOUT TO REBOUND BACK AT US AS ENERGY AND CONVERGE ON A QUANTUM SINGULARITY! WE'RE TALKING A VERY BIG BANG HERE!

OH, COME ON. HOW BAD COULD IT BE?

TORG, SOMETIMES I WONDER WHY I TALK SO MUCH.
YEAH, ENOUGH OF YOUR JIBBER-JABBER!

OFFICIAL SLUGGY FREELANCE FOURTH ANNIVERSARY COMIC

*SUNG TO THE TUNE OF "FOR HE'S A JOLLY GOOD FELLOW."

CRASH!

YOU PARKED THIS SHIP ON MY THIGH!

YOU PARKED THIS SHIP ON MY THIGH, YOU PARKED THIS SHIP ON MY THIGH, FOUR YEARS OF NIFTY DARN CO-O-MICS, YOU PARKED THIS SHIP ON MY THIGH. **

**STILL SUNG TO THE TUNE OF "FOR HE'S A JOLLY GOOD FELLOW."

I'M READY TO GO. WHERE ARE THE GUYS?
I SENT THEM HOME WITHOUT US.

WHAT?!?
I DID IT FOR YOU! FOR OUR LOVE!

...WHAT?!?
YOU SAID YOU'D GIVE ME A KISS IF I WAS THE LAST MAN IN THE UNIVERSE, AND I AM!

I SAID I WOULDN'T KISS YOU EVEN IF YOU WERE THE LAST MAN IN THE UNIVERSE!!!
OH.
WARNING! CONVERGENCE IMMINENT!

NEVER MIND.
DIE! DIE! DIE!

SLUGGY FREELANCE
A VERY BIG BANG!

A MIXTURE OF MATTER AND ENERGY IS SENT HURLING TOWARDS THE EDGES OF THE UNIVERSE, WHERE IT RICOCHETS AGAIN.

IT AGAIN CONVERGES ON THE QUANTUM SINGULARITY, CAUSING ANOTHER VERY BIG BANG.

ANOTHER RICOCHET.

ANOTHER VERY BIG BANG.

RICOCHET.

BIG BANG.

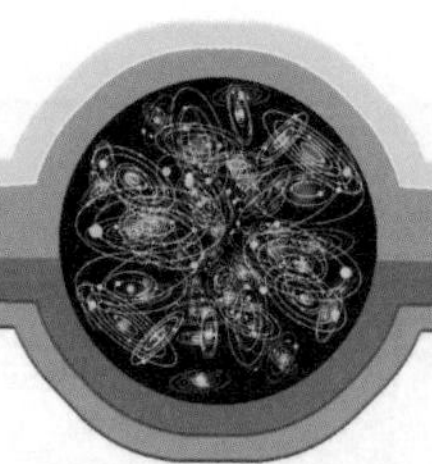

EPILOGUE
IT'S WORKING? IT'S WORKING?!?
RICOCHET.

IT JUST STARTED LAST NIGHT! THE ENERGY YIELD IS NOMINAL, BUT THE INTERNAL ENERGY IS PHENOMENAL!
BIG BANG.

CONGRATULATIONS! YOU'VE PROVEN A MICRO-GALACTIC ECO-BATTERY CAN WORK!
RICOCHET.

WHAT STARTED THE REACTION?
WE DON'T KNOW. ACCORDING TO THE COMPUTER AI, IT WAS "SHEER STUPIDITY". WE'RE CHECKING IT FOR ERRORS. IN ANY CASE WE'RE CLOSE!
BIG BANG.

NOT CLOSE ENOUGH, I'M AFRAID. THIS EXPENSIVE EXPERIMENT HAS TAKEN FAR TOO MUCH TIME. WE'RE PULLING YOUR PET PROJECT!
NO!
RICOCHET.

WHEN WE'RE SO CLOSE TO A POWER SOURCE CAPABLE OF PROVIDING PORTABLE HAPPINESS TO SO MANY OF OUR PEOPLE? ESPECIALLY ME?
BIG BANG.

VOZAR, YOU'RE JUST GOING TO HAVE TO PLUG YOUR WAFFLE IRON INTO THE WALL LIKE EVERYBODY ELSE.
SOUND AND FURY FARMS
WAFFLES
RESEARCH AND DEVELOPMENT
THE END

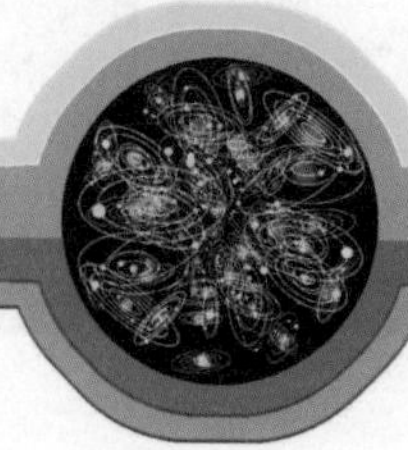

YOU'RE HOME! YAY!
YOU LAND YOUR SPACESHIP ON MY LEG AND THINK SAYING "SORRY" IS ENOUGH?
IF THE MAJORITY OF THE SHIP'S WEIGHT WAS ON YOUR LEG YOU WOULDN'T *HAVE* BOTH YOUR LEGS RIGHT NOW. YOU JUST GOT A LITTLE BRUISE.
IT STILL HURT!
Poing Poing Poing

LIKE I SAID, I'M SORRY.
WELL, I'M GLAD YOU GUYS MADE IT BACK IN ONE PIECE. BUT NOW IT IS TIME FOR YOU TO TAKE YOUR DIMENSIONAL FLUX AGITATOR AND GO. SASHA IS WAITING OUTSIDE. I'VE ALREADY NOTIFIED SECURITY.
WOW, AYLEE'S WEB DESIGN BUSINESS MUST BE GOING WELL TO AFFORD REDECORATING MY APARTMENT! LOOKS VERY HIGH-TECH BUSINESSEY!

ALTHOUGH THE SECURITY GUARDS ARE A BIT OF OVERKILL!
EXIT

I'M SO GLAD YOU GUYS ARE ALIVE! WHAT HAPPENED? MY REMOTE DIDN'T WORK RIGHT, DID IT?

YOUR REMOTE WORKED FINE. WE RAN INTO...OTHER PROBLEMS. IT'S A GREAT STORY FOR LATER, BUT NOW I JUST WANT TO GO HOME AND REST.
EASY FOR YOU! GWYNN JUST HAD ME THROWN OUT OF MY APARTMENT!
GUYS, YOU'VE BEEN GONE FOR MONTHS, AND A LOT HAS CHANGED. YOU, UM... DON'T HAVE HOMES ANYMORE.

AYLEE'S DONE PHENOMENALLY WELL FINANCIALLY AND SHE BOUGHT THE APARTMENT COMPLEX. SOME BUILDINGS LIKE YOURS HAVE BEEN MADE INTO OFFICE SPACE, AND OTHERS ARE KEPT AS APARTMENTS FOR HER MANY EMPLOYEES.

YOU'RE KIDDING ME!
NO, AND MAYBE WE SHOULD GET MOVING. MY SECURITY PASS TO BE ON THE GREEN IS EXPIRING IN 58 SECONDS.

57, 56, 55, 54...
SECURITY

AYLEE CAN'T JUST THROW ALL OUR STUFF INTO STORAGE AND STEAL OUR HOMES! I MISS MY BED!
I GUESS YOU GUYS COULD SUE AYLEE...?
NO. BUT I *DO* NEED TO TALK TO HER.
GOOD LUCK. I HAVEN'T SEEN HER IN MONTHS. NOBODY GETS IN TO SEE AYLEE THESE DAYS.
NOBODY WILL WHEN I GET A HOLD OF HER, MESSING WITH MY STUFF AND ALL!
GWYNN LETS ME IN SOMETIMES BUT I HAVEN'T SEEN AYLEE EITHER.

HOW DID ZOË TAKE BEING EVICTED?
SHE WASN'T HERE, TORG. SHE WENT HOME.
OH, THAT'S GREAT. SHE'S VISITING HER FOLKS IN... WHERE DO THEY LIVE AGAIN?
NEBRASKA.
...NEBRASKA, AND WHEN SHE COMES BACK FOR SCHOOL, SHE'S GOING TO FIND THIS MESS.
NO, TORG. SHE'S GOING TO SCHOOL OUT THERE. SHE COULDN'T AFFORD COLLEGE HERE WITHOUT HER SCHOLARSHIP. SHE'S NOT COMING BACK.

SO, ANYONE ELSE UP FOR POP-TARTS?

A MONTH AGO:
I'M HOME!
HI HONEY! IT'S GREAT TO SEE YOU!
HI DADDY!
HI MOM...?
SHE'S GIVING YOU THE SILENT TREATMENT
I'M KIND OF RELIEVED.
YOUR HAND DOESN'T LOOK BROKEN ENOUGH THAT YOU COULDN'T PICK UP A PHONE!

MIN!
ZOË! I NEVER THOUGHT YOU'D COME HOME!
I WORK MY FINGERS TO THE BONE FOR YOU AND YOU IGNORE ME.

HOW'S MY LIL' SIS?
LOOKING FORWARD TO SENIOR YEAR, CATCHING SOME FLAK SINCE DAD SWITCHED TO TEACHING HIGH SCHOOL ENGLISH.
YOU'LL UNDERSTAND WHEN YOU HAVE KIDS OF YOUR OWN!

MOM'S GIVING YOU THE SILENT TREATMENT, HUH?
YEAH. LOUDEST ONE EVER.
DOESN'T BOTHER ME. NOT ONE BIT!

IT'S NEVER BEEN THE SAME SINCE YOU GOT HER THAT SIGN-MAKER PROGRAM FOR HER PRINTER.
NEXT YEAR I'M GETTING HER DIABLO 2.
I BLAME MYSELF. AND SATAN.

ZOË, I ONLY GAVE YOU THE SILENT TREATMENT BECAUSE YOU DIDN'T CALL BEFORE YOU... EYAAAA!
EYYYAAAAH!

MOM! KNOCK BEFORE ENTERING! I WAS CHANGING!
WHUMP!

I COVERED MYSELF QUICK! SHE COULDN'T HAVE SEEN THE TATTOO ON MY CHEST ...COULD SHE HAVE?
MY OWN FLESH AND BLOOD...BODILY MUTILATION...
ACK*

GOOD LORD, I'VE KILLED MY OWN MOTHER.

SLUGGY FREELANCE
ORIENTATION TODAY!

I GUESS I COULDN'T KEEP MY TATTOO A SECRET FOREVER.
YOU GUYS DIDN'T HAVE TO COME WITH ME FOR THIS, YOU KNOW!
WE ALL WANTED TO COME, DIDN'T WE?
SURE!
OF COURSE!

HOLD ON A SECOND! EXCUSE ME, I'VE GOT SOMETHING IMPORTANT TO DO OVER THERE.

WHAT?
BE OVER THERE.
YEAH, ME TOO! PRIOR ENGAGEMENT.

THERE'S NO CHANCE OF GETTING YOU TO GIVE ME THE SILENT TREATMENT WHILE CHECKING IN FOR ORIENTATION IS THERE?
EVERY TIME YOU MUTILATE YOUR BODY YOU MAY AS WELL BE MUTILATING MY HEART!

AND YOU ARE...
I'M ZOË. THERE I AM!

AH, A TRANSFER STUDENT! WELCOME! I'M IAN, YOUR ORIENTATION PAL! HAVE YOU MADE UP YOUR MIND ABOUT LIVING ON CAMPUS? WE ONLY HAVE A FEW ROOMS LEFT IN ANTMIKAL HALL, SO IF YOU WANT TO LIVE ON CAMPUS...
EVEN THOUGH SHE LIVES NOT FORTY MINUTES FROM HOME, SHE WANTS TO LIVE ON CAMPUS. I GUESS SHE DOES WHATEVER SHE WANTS WITH HER BODY, SHE MAY AS WELL DO WHAT EVER SHE WANTS WITH HER LIFE!
S-Z

ON CAMPUS.

GREAT, I'LL SIGN YOU UP NOW!
WHAT HURTS THE MOST IS THAT YOU'D DO THAT TO YOURSELF BEHIND MY BACK! DON'T YOU KNOW HOW WORRIED I AM ABOUT YOU?
LOOK, MOM, I DIDN'T MEAN FOR IT TO HAPPEN.

OH, SO YOU ACCIDENTALLY GOT A NOSE PIERCING?
WHAT?
YOU THINK BY NOT WEARING A NOSE RING IN THE HOUSE I WOULDN'T NOTICE?

THAT'S... THAT'S WHAT THIS WAS ALL ABOUT! MOM, THAT'S NOT A NOSE PIERCING! IT'S...

SHHHH! IT'S A SMALL PIMPLE.

A PIMPLE? A PIMPLE?!? YOU THINK I DON'T KNOW THE DIFFERENCE BETWEEN A NOSE-PIERCING AND A PIMPLE?!?!?

OH WAIT! YOU'RE RIGHT!

I'M SO SORRY! I'M SUCH A HORRIBLE MOTHER! BUT IT WAS AN HONEST MISTAKE, HONEY!

DOESN'T THAT PIMPLE LOOK LIKE A NOSE PIERCING TO YOU?
I... HAVE NO IDEA.

WELL, THANK GOD MY DAUGHTER JUST HAS PIMPLES, INSTEAD OF BEING ONE OF THOSE PIERCED FREAKS!
ZOË, THIS WILL BE YOUR NEW ROOMMATE, KIT.

ZOË'S OLD HIGH SCHOOL:
MY DAUGHTER HAS COME BY TO TAKE ME OUT TO LUNCH! WHAT A PLEASANT SURPRISE!

WELL, COLLEGE STARTS NEXT WEEK, DAD! I WANTED TO SPEND SOME TIME WITH YOU BEFORE I GO! WOW, BEING BACK AT HIGH SCHOOL SURE BRINGS BACK MEMORIES! IN OTHER WORDS, LET'S GET OUT OF HERE!

I HAVE A CLASS IN FIVE MINUTES. AFTERWARDS WE'LL GRAB A BITE. OK?

THESE SUMMER SESSION CLASSES ARE JUST PLAIN CREEPY. I THOUGHT SUMMER SCHOOL WAS JUST FOR BAD STUDENTS, LIKE THAT GUY I DATED. WHAT WAS HIS NAME...?

CLEM!
ZOË!

AH HEARD YOU WUZ BACK IN TOWN! STOPPED BY TO SEE YER OLD BEAU CLEM, HUH?
CLEM, WE ONLY WENT OUT ON ONE DATE. YOU WERE NEVER MY "BEAU".

YEAH, WHUT WENT WRONG WITH "US"?
FOR STARTERS, YOU USE WORDS LIKE "BEAU".
SO, YOU...UM ARE *STILL* IN HIGH SCHOOL? I THOUGHT YOU DROPPED OUT JUNIOR YEAR!
NOSIREE, I AIN'T GOIN' TA SCHOOL HERE, ZOË! **I WORK HERE!** AND I WUSSN'T AS DUMB AS YOU THOUGHT!

CLEM, YOU'RE HOLDING ROADKILL.
AH NEVER SAID MY JOB WUZ EASY.

HI, DR. SCASINO!
LET ME KNOW 'BOUT THEM LAB RESULTS, IF YA WANT EXTRA CREDIT, JUAN!
WILL DO!

"DR. SCASINO"?

IT MIGHT SURPRISE YA TA KNOW, ZOË, I DIDN'T DROP OUT OF HIGH SCHOOL! AH GOT INTA COLLEGE EARLY. LAST YEAR AH GOT MY DOC'TOR'ATE IN BIOLOGY AND NOW AH'M GIVING A YEAR BACK TA THA COMMUNITY AS THE BIOLOGY TEACHER HERE B'FORE GOIN' ABROAD.

SO, WHAT DO YA THINK OF YER OLD BEAU NOW?
CLEM, YOU'RE STILL HOLDING ROADKILL.
THIS IS FER ADULT STEM-CELL RESEARCH, PIMPLE-NOSE!

TOO YOUNG? COLLEGE IS A YEAR AWAY FOR ME, MOM!
I DON'T WANT YOU HANGING AROUND ZOË'S COLLEGE FRIENDS. THEY ARE **NOT** GOOD PEOPLE!

AT FIRST ZOË WAS NERVOUS ABOUT HER NEW SCHOOL, AND THE NORMALITY SURROUNDING HER.

ZOË, WHY ARE YOU EYEING THAT SQUIRREL LIKE HE'S GOING TO ATTACK YOU?

BUT SOON IT WAS LIKE A NEW HOME, QUIET AND PEACEFUL.

PEACEFUL, DESPITE DR. CLEM'S CONSTANT ATTENTION.

SHE KEPT IN TOUCH WITH HER FAMILY.

GOT ALONG WELL WITH HER ROOM-MATE, KIT.

HER SCHOOLWORK IMPROVED DRAMATICALLY.

AND NOT LONG AFTER THAT, TORG, RIFF, AND BUN-BUN RETURNED, AND ZOË WAS VERY RELIEVED TO KNOW THEY WERE SAFE AND SOUND.

ZOË! THANK GOD YOU PICKED UP! WE REALLY NEEDED TO TALK TO YOU!
WHAT IS IT, TORG? WHAT'S WRONG?

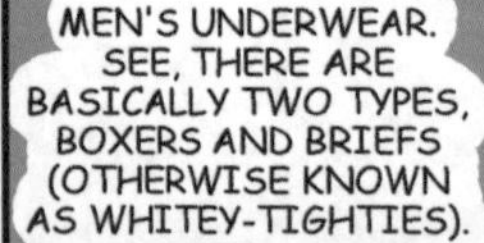

MEN'S UNDERWEAR. SEE, THERE ARE BASICALLY TWO TYPES, BOXERS AND BRIEFS (OTHERWISE KNOWN AS WHITEY-TIGHTIES).

NOW, BOXERS COME IN ALL DIFFERENT DESIGNS AND PATTERNS AND DIFFERENT MATERIALS LIKE COTTON AND SILK. A MAN CAN STILL BE A MAN AND WEAR SILK BOXERS.

MEN CAN'T WEAR SILK WHITEY-TIGHTIES, 'CAUSE THEN THEY'D BE PANTIES.

THAT WAS IT.

click

I MISS THOSE GUYS.

BYE, ZOË!... I MISS YOU TOO... I'LL TELL THEM... BYE!

NOW THAT I KNOW ZOË'S OK, I HAVE TIME TO WORRY ABOUT AYLEE. BUT THE FIRST THING WE'VE GOT TO DO IS FIND A NEW PLACE TO LIVE!
WHY DON'T WE STAY HERE WITH SASHA? SHE DOESN'T MIND, AND I LIKE IT HERE.

THAT'S FINE FOR YOU, SINCE **YOU** DON'T HAVE TO SLEEP IN THE TUB!
YOU DON'T *HAVE* TO SLEEP IN THE TUB; WE JUST THOUGHT IT WAS FUNNY!

WHY DON'T WE JUST FIND A NEW APARTMENT IN THE NEWSPAPER?
USING A REALTOR TO FIND US A HOME WILL SAVE US VALUABLE TIME!

BEFORE WE BEGIN FINDING YOU A HOME I NEED SOME PRIVATE INFORMATION ON YOU, TORG!

WHUMP!
INDENTURY

I HAVE TO FILL OUT ***ALL THOSE FORMS?***
NO, THEY'RE FILLED OUT ALREADY. I WAS ABLE TO GET ALL YOUR PRIVATE DATA ONLINE WITH JUST A FEW CLICKS OF THE MOUSE.
OH THANK GOD!
INDENTURY 21

SO TELL ME, WHAT ARE YOU TWO LOOKING FOR IN A HOME?

ROBO T.V.

I KNOW JUST THE PLACE.

IT'S PINK!
I'VE HEARD PINK CAN SOOTHE THE INSANE.

WE'VE BEEN LOOKING AT HOUSES ALL WEEK, BUT YOU MAY WANT TO MOVE ON THIS NUMBER! I THINK TWO OTHER COUPLES HAVE ALREADY BID ON IT.
THIS ONE IS LISTED AS "HAVING A GREAT PERSONALITY", RIGHT?

HEY! IT HAS INDOOR PLUMBING!
AND A BOATLOAD OF CHARM! IT PRETTY MUCH HAS EVERY-THING YOU NEED!

I HATE TO SOUND LIKE A BROKEN RECORD, BUT WHERE'S THE FIREMAN'S POLE?
FOR THE LAST TIME, NO HOUSE COMES WITH THAT, TORG!
WHAT DO YOU MEAN "OTHER COUPLES"?

LOUIS, THESE GUYS ARE DRIVING ME NUTS! I'M THINKING OF KICKING THEM TO REAM-AXE REALTY.
DON'T EVEN THINK ABOUT IT! WE JUST CONFIRMED WITH THE BANK. TORG'S ASSETS ARE MINIMAL BECAUSE THEY ARE ALL TIED UP WITH THE PLANET'S FASTEST GROWING INTERNET COMPANY!
DON'T LIKE IT
TOO BAROQUE
FOR SALE

IT'S THE ONLY DOT-COM WITH MOMENTUM LIKE THIS; ITS STOCKS ARE SOARING EVEN IN THIS ECONOMY! HE'S BEEN PRE-APPROVED FOR A MORTGAGE UP TO... THREE TRILLION DOLLARS!

CHA-CHING!

EEK! HER IRISES AND PUPILS JUST TURNED INTO DOLLAR SIGNS!
DEMON REALTOR! DEMON REALTOR!
OW! OW! OW! IT ALWAYS GIVES ME AN ICE-CREAM HEADACHE WHEN THAT HAPPENS!

WOW! A POOL WITH WET-BAR AND A FIREPOLE! THIS HOUSE RULES!
I LOVE IT! BUT I THINK THIS IS A LITTLE PRICIER THAN I EXPECTED.

I'M SURE SOMEONE OF YOUR MEANS WILL FIND THE MONTHLY COSTS MORE THAN AFFORDABLE! PLUS THIS HOUSE'S PREVIOUS OWNER IS AN UNKNOWN CELEBRITY!
MY CAREER IS DOING FINE. WHY DON'T YOU KEEP YOUR OPINIONS TO YOURSELF?

NO, MR. SHEEN! YOU REQUESTED YOUR IDENTITY REMAIN "UNKNOWN" FOR PRIVACY PURPOSES.
OH. RIGHT. SORRY.

HOLY CRAP! THAT WAS EMILIO ESTEVEZ!
CHARLIE SHEEN!

WHAT'S THIS SERIAL NUMBER HERE?
THAT'S NOT A SERIAL NUMBER! THAT'S A TOTAL COST OF OUR NON-ARBITRARY FEES!
DING

WELL, MY BAD FOR JUMPING OUT OF THE CLOSET EARLY, BUT WE ALL KNOW YOU WERE GOING TO SIGN IT, WE'RE ALL WITNESSES, SO WE'LL JUST PRETEND YOU DID.

WE GOING OUT TONIGHT?
NOT TONIGHT, SASHA. TORG AND I ARE GOING TO PARTY WITH CHARLIE SHEEN!

WHAT'S WITH THE PLIERS?
ARE YOU DEAF? I SAID WE'RE PARTYING WITH CHARLIE SHEEN.

I BROUGHT THE CRATE OF LEDER-HOSEN!
GUYS, CHARLIE SHEEN'S BEEN CLEAN AND SOBER FOR YEARS NOW.

OH... MAYBE HE HAS THE ADDRESS OF ROBERT DOWNEY JR.?
WHERE ARE WE GOING TO FIND A BELT SANDER AND A PORTUGUESE MAN-OF-WAR AT THIS TIME OF NIGHT?

HI! WE'RE HERE ABOUT THE AD IN THE NEWSPAPER! TO LOOK AT THE HOUSE YOU'RE RENTING!

WOW! BIG!

IT IS PARTIALLY FURNISHED AND IS AVAILABLE FOR RENTING IMMEDIATELY. THE PRIOR OCCUPANTS LEFT... ABRUPTLY.

I GATHERED THAT FROM THE HALF-EATEN SANDWICHES STILL LYING ON THE KITCHEN COUNTER.

SANDWICHES? THE HOUSE COMES WITH SANDWICHES? WE'RE SOLD!

GUYS, THOSE SANDWICHES WERE LEFT HALF-EATEN BY THE PREVIOUS TENANTS! SOMETHING MOTIVATED THEM TO UP AND LEAVE IN THE MIDDLE OF A MEAL! DOESN'T THAT TELL YOU ANYTHING?
HMMMPH, NOT ENOUGH MAYO.

SO, WHAT DO YOU SAY?
WE'LL TAKE IT!

I ADMIT THE HOUSE IS CHEAP TO LEASE FOR THE SPACE, BUT CAN YOU TWO AFFORD IT?
IT'S GOT ENOUGH BEDROOMS; WE'LL NEED A COUPLE OF ROOMMATES.

COUNT ME OUT. I LIKE MY APARTMENT.
WHO CAN WE GET ON SHORT NOTICE?

I THINK I SPEAK FOR MY CROTCH AS WELL WHEN I SAY WE ACCEPT YOUR OFFER OF LODGINGS!

VERY WELL, WELCOME TO YOUR NEW HOME. THIS IS THE MASTER KEY. IT UNLOCKS AND LOCKS ALL THE DOORS.

ALL, THAT IS, EXCEPT FOR THE AREA THAT IS SECTIONED OFF AND BOARDED UP. NOBODY GOES THERE.

NOBODY?
WELL, AT LEAST NONE OF THE COOL PEOPLE. SOME REALLY UNCOOL LOSERS DO, BUT WE MAKE FUN OF THEM.

YEAH, ONLY LOSERS GO INTO THE FORBIDDEN SECTIONS OF THE HOUSE.
YEAH! YEAH!
crotch.
EXCELLENT.

YOU'RE ACTUALLY ROOMING WITH BERT? THE GUY WHO'S ALL "CROTCH THIS" AND "CROTCH THAT"?
HE'S OK ONCE YOU GET TO KNOW HIM.

ACTUALLY, I TAKE THAT BACK. HE'S OK AS LONG AS YOU DON'T GET TO KNOW HIM.
WHO'S YOUR FOURTH ROOM-MATE?

DON'T KNOW. BERT SAID HE KNEW SOMEONE WHO NEEDED A PLACE.
HI, TORG!

ANGELA?!?

ANGELA? SHE'S OUT OF THE ASYLUM?
ZOË WANTS TO KNOW HOW YOU GOT OUT OF THE NUTHOUSE!
TORG, I'M HANGING UP ON YOU NOW.
CLICK

WHOA! THAT CHILL I GOT CAN MEAN ONE OF TWO THINGS. AN UNEASY SPIRIT LURKS AROUND ME, OR SOMEONE OUT THERE IS START-ING A RECAP.
ANGELA, HOW HAVE YOU BEEN? WE HAD A LOT OF FUN LAST SUMMER, IN THAT CABIN IN THE WOODS, BEFORE THOSE SATANSPAWN KITTENS STARTED ALL THAT MUTILATION AND DEATH. LAST I HEARD, YOU DEVELOPED A MASSIVE PHOBIA OF KITTENS AND HAD TO SPEND TIME IN A MENTAL INSTITUTION!
THAT'S WHY I GOT KOJI HERE, FOR PROTECTION! I'VE BEEN OUT FOR A WHILE. I SHOULD HAVE CALLED, BUT I NEEDED TIME BEFORE FACING YOU GUYS. IT REALLY HURT TO LOSE DEX. I THINK I REALLY LOVED HIM! I MEAN, NOT THAT I DIDN'T LIKE THE TIME WE SPENT TOGETHER OR ANYTHING, NO OFFENSE.
wuf.
NONE TAKEN.

YES, WELL ...UM
SO...

SMOOCH!

Sluggy Freelance
OOOOOH!
SO, THIS IS THE NEW PLACE. DEPRESSING. NEEDS MORE CHICKS.
WELL, WE'RE ALL MOVED IN!
NOT ALL, I STILL HAVE TO SET UP MY WORKSHOP. MAYBE I'LL WORK ON THAT LATER.
I THINK I'M GOING TO SLEEP LIKE THE DEAD TONIGHT!
BERT'S ALREADY OUT.
UGH... GROGGY... MUST GET LATE NIGHT SNACK...
PEANUT BUTTER AND JELLY SOUNDS GOOD.
GUESS ANGELA COULDN'T SLEEP EITHER.
WHY IS SHE SOBBING?
I DON'T CARE WHAT YOU THINK, I *KNOW* WHAT I SAW, AND ANGELA JUST LOOKS **BAD** WITHOUT MAKEUP!
YEAH, LIKE SASHA DOESN'T USE MORE EYE -LINER THAN OUR ENTIRE LOCAL ROCKY HORROR ENSEMBLE.

SO, IF THAT WASN'T YOU RIFF SAW THE OTHER NIGHT, I WONDER WHO IT WAS.
I DON'T KNOW. I DON'T THINK I...

OH, TORG...
WHAT IS IT, ANGELA?

SOMETHING'S WRONG WITH THIS HOUSE. IT FRIGHTENS ME.
YOU'VE BEEN THROUGH SO MUCH, AND THIS *IS* AN OLD HOUSE. MAYBE YOU'RE JUST HYPER-SENSITIVE.

SOMETHING'S WRONG WITH THIS SANDWICH. IT FRIGHTENS ME.
BANANA-KETCHUP IS A SCARY CONDIMENT UNTIL YOU LEARN TO EMBRACE IT.

HI, ANGELA!
EEEK!
grrrrrr

KOJI, I'M SORRY THAT ANGELA'S SO AFRAID OF THIS HOUSE.
wuf.

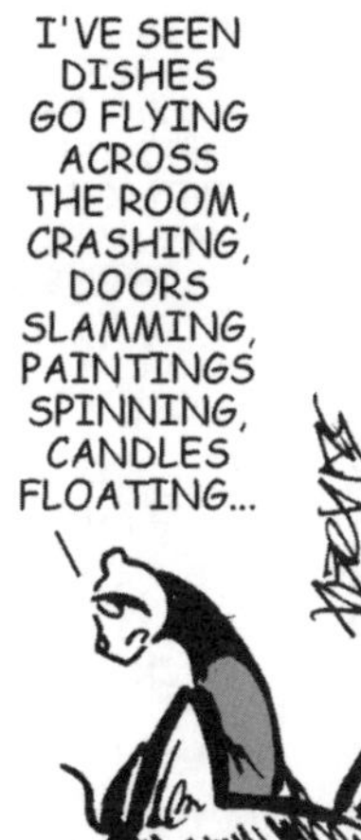
I'VE SEEN DISHES GO FLYING ACROSS THE ROOM, CRASHING, DOORS SLAMMING, PAINTINGS SPINNING, CANDLES FLOATING...

IT'S THE BESTEST HOUSE *EVER!*
IT'S NOT LIKE THERE'S ANYTHING SCARY GOING ON, LIKE DOING LAUNDRY!

OR WAITING IN LINE AT THE DMV!
EEEK!

IT'S BEEN A FEW DAYS AND NOTHING WEIRD HAS HAPPENED. I GUESS YOU WERE RIGHT. I WAS OVERREACTING. I'M SORRY!
IT'S OK. WOMEN OFTEN RESPOND TO THE UNKNOWN WITH FEAR!

AHEM. TORG? TELL HER.
TELL ME WHAT?

ANGELA, YOU HAVE YOUR OWN BATHROOM. WE THREE GUYS HAVE TO SHARE THE OTHER ONE, SO COULD YOU PLEASE STOP HANGING YOUR PANTYHOSE OVER OUR SHOWER-CURTAIN?
THOSE AREN'T MINE!
UNHAND MY PROPERTY, KNAVES!

YEEEK!

SO, ONLY *WOMEN* RESPOND TO THE UNKNOWN WITH FEAR, HUH?
MEN RESPOND TO THE *"DON'T WANNA KNOW."*

HI DER, FRAU-LOIN! I'D LIKE TO MAKEN AN APPOINTMENT DER TO SEE DE C.E.A. OF YER COMPANY.
"C.E.A.?"
CHIEF EXECUTIVE ALIEN.

I TOLD YOU! AYLEE ISN'T TAKING YOUR CALLS AND DOESN'T MEET IN PERSON WITH ANYONE! SHE DOESN'T NEED YOU ANYMORE; SHE'S A BUSINESS SUCCESS ON HER OWN, TORG!

WHO'S-A THIS "TORG"? MAMA MIA, I ALREADY TELL YOU; I'M TURG LE TURGTURG, SWEDISH WEBDESIGN GURU! I COME DER IN PEACE-EN!
IS THAT SUPPOSED TO BE A SWEDISH ACCENT? WHAT THE HELL KIND OF ACCENT IS THAT, ANYWAY? BYE TORG.
CLICK

"TURG LE TURGTURG?"
YOU WERE MUCH MORE BELIEVABLE, O AMBASSADOR FROM CASTLE RIFFENSTEIN.

BYE ANGELA! AFTER WORK I'LL PICK YOU UP FOR A MOVIE?
SOUNDS GREAT! BYE, TORG!

SO, YOU'RE DATING ANGELA? I THOUGHT YOU LOVED ZOË!

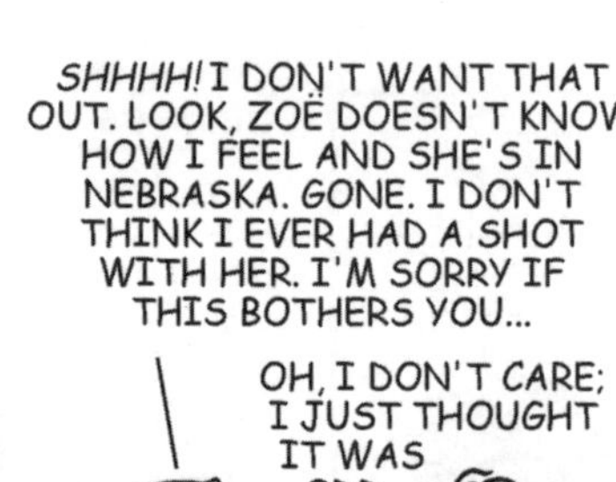
SHHHH! I DON'T WANT THAT OUT. LOOK, ZOË DOESN'T KNOW HOW I FEEL AND SHE'S IN NEBRASKA. GONE. I DON'T THINK I EVER HAD A SHOT WITH HER. I'M SORRY IF THIS BOTHERS YOU...

OH, I DON'T CARE; I JUST THOUGHT IT WAS ODD.

YOU'RE A WEIRD GIRL, SASHA.
THAT DOESN'T BOTHER ME EITHER.

WE KNOW FROM GWYNN THAT AYLEE IS ON THE TOP FLOOR OF HER MAIN BUILDING, WHICH USED TO BE YOUR APARTMENT BUILDING. AND THAT SHE DOESN'T SEE ANYBODY, EVER. AND THAT SECURITY IS TIGHT.

I KNOW YOU'RE WORRIED ABOUT HER, TORG. WHAT I DON'T UNDERSTAND IS WHAT YOU WANT TO DO ABOUT IT.

I WANT TO INITIATE.... OPERATION HIDDEN HERALD!

"HIDDEN HERALD?"
THAT'S MY CODENAME. FOR I ALONE MUST SNEAK INTO AYLEE'S OFFICE BUILDING SO I CAN TALK TO HER, FACE-TO-FACE, AND FIND OUT WHAT'S GOING ON.

"HIDDEN HERALD?"
TODAY'S SESAME-STREET WAS BROUGHT TO TORG BY THE LETTER "H".
AM I LATE FOR OPERATION "HORKY HAM-HEAD?"

IT'S BEEN TWO DAYS SINCE THE START OF **OPERATION HIDDEN HERALD.** LET'S BEGIN WITH OUR INDIVIDUAL RECONNAISSANCE REPORTS. I'LL GO FIRST.

"**OPERATION RUN-AROUND-WILLY-NILLY** REVEALED THAT THE GUARDS ARE ALERT AND DON'T PACK LETHAL FORCE."

"THEY ARE, HOWEVER ARMED WITH PAINFUL TASERS."

A MARGINAL SUCCESS. TORG?

"**OPERATION LOOK-I'M-TOM-CRUISE** NEVER GOT BEYOND TESTING PHASE."
WHY ARE WE ON SASHA'S APARTMENT'S SKYLIGHT?
PRACTICING A ROOF-ENTRY ON AYLEE'S BUILDING.

WHRRRR!
SLUGGY FREELANCE

NEAT!
WHAP!
"DAMN INCH TO METRIC BUNGEE CONVERSIONS!"

YOU GAVE UP AFTER ONE TRY?
I JUST BECAME CONSCIOUS AN HOUR AGO. SASHA?

"**OPERATION NEVER-SEND-A-MAN-TO-DO-A-WOMAN'S-JOB** WAS A CRUCIAL SUCCESS. I HAD LUNCH WITH GWYNN UNDER THE GUISE OF MAKING FUN OF RIFF'S GENERAL BEHAVIOR."
"HEY!"
Duh Duh Duh

"THIS GAVE ME ACCESS TO SNAP SOME PICTURES AROUND THE LOBBY."

I THINK YOU GUYS WILL BE MOST INTERESTED IN *THIS* PICTURE.

A WEAK SPOT. YOU NEED A KEY-CARD TO GET PAST THESE DOORS, BUT ONCE IN, THE AIR VENTS LOOK UNPROTECTED.

I DON'T THINK TORG WILL BE ABLE TO NAVIGATE A MAZE OF AIR VENTS.
HE'LL HAVE TO GET AS CLOSE AS HE CAN TO THE TOP FLOOR FIRST.
I'M NOT SURE I CAN EVEN FIT IN THAT VENT!
I'LL DO IT.

I CAN FIT THROUGH THE VENTS. BESIDES, I CAN GET TORG PAST THE TASER-GUARDS NO PROBLEM. THE WAY I SEE IT, YOU CAN'T MAKE IT WITHOUT ME.
AGREED. BUN-BUN TAKES CARE OF THE GUARDS. I GET A HOLD OF GWYNN'S KEYCARD, AND SNEAK PAST THE FIRST CHECK-POINT. I GET AS CLOSE AS I CAN TO THE TOP FLOOR, THEN SEND BUN-BUN IN THROUGH AN AIR VENT.

I LOCATE ZUCCHINI-FACE AND OPEN THE WAY FOR NERD-BOY TO COME IN AND TALK SOME SENSE INTO HER BEFORE I RIP HER INTO PIECES FOR MESSING WITH MY STUFF.

HOW ARE WE GOING TO GET THE KEYCARD FROM GWYNN?
I'LL SEDUCE HER.

MAN, HOW HARD DID YOU HIT YOUR HEAD ON SASHA'S FLOOR?
I KNOW I DON'T HAVE MUCH OF A CHANCE OF SEDUCING GWYNN, BUT IF I PULLED IT OFF, WOULDN'T I BE COOL?
YOU WANT THIS WHOLE OPERATION TO HINGE ON ACTING COOL?

I WANT TO TRY! I WANT TO TRY!
I CALLED IT FIRST.

THE GUARDS CHANGE SHIFTS IN FIVE MINUTES. IF YOU MAKE A BEELINE TO THE LOBBY, YOU GUYS SHOULDN'T RUN INTO ANY TROUBLE.
UP
EX

TAKE THIS KNOCKOUT SPRAY IN CASE YOUR PLAN TO SEDUCE GWYNN FAILS. ONE SPRITZ IN THE FACE WILL KNOCK HER OUT FOR HOURS. THIS IS A RELATIVELY NEW FORMULA SO BE SURE TO USE AS LITTLE OF IT AS POSSIBLE.

THIS IS GWYNN WE'RE TALKING ABOUT. WHAT IF SHE CHARGES?
EMPTY THE CAN AT HER. GOD SPEED.

HEY THERE HOT STUFF!
TORG, YOU HAVE FIVE SECONDS TO EXPLAIN WHAT YOU'RE DOING HERE BEFORE I CALL SECURITY.

YOU'RE LOOKING SO, UM, FINE...AND ...STUFF... WORDS...

YAAA!
ssst.
ARGH!

CLONG!
SMASH!
YEE AAA AAEE

THIS ISN'T KNOCKOUT SPRAY! IT'S WINTERGREEN BINACA.
WHUMP

GOT THE KEYCARD. I'M IN.
OK, LOOKING GOOD. KEEP MOVING AND YOU'LL BE IN GOOD SHAPE.
ROGER.

JUST CALLED UP A FLOOR PLAN, AND YOU HAVE SOME SECURITY MEASURES AHEAD. BE CAREFUL.
ALWAYS AM.

THE CLOCK IS TICKING, BUT KEEP YOUR COOL AND YOU'LL MAKE IT OUT ALIVE.
YOU'VE REACHED THE END OF SIDE A.

CLICKITY-CLACK

I'M COUNTING ON YOU. WE'RE ALL COUNTING ON YOU.
WHAT THE HELL ARE YOU LISTENING TO?
INSPIRATIONAL ESPIONAGE TAPE FOR THE SPY ON A BUDGET.
ONS
EVEL
B37

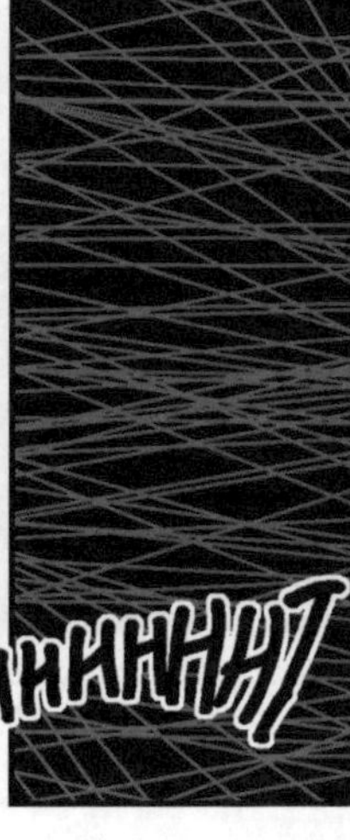

OK, IT WASN'T A MAP OF THE VENT SYSTEM. IT WAS A MAZE OF TORG'S THOUGHT PATTERN.

AND YOU KICKED ME AND MY BOYS OUT OF OUR HOME AND MESSED WITH OUR STUFF WHILE I WAS TRAPPED IN SOME STUPID DIMENSION. YOU KNOW WHAT A LOUSY HOME-COMING THAT WAS?

US FIGHTING HERE IN MY PLACE OF BUSINESS, A LOSE-LOSE FOR ME. TEN G'S IN AN OFFSHORE ACCOUNT AS AN APOLOGY FROM ME TO YOU.

WORKS FOR ME.

DON'T TROUBLE YOURSELF WITH THE VENTS. YOU CAN WALK OUT THE FRONT DOOR. TELL TORG; IF I FIND HIM NOSING IN MY BUSINESS AGAIN I'M GOING TO GNAW HIS HEAD OFF

HI, AYLEE! I NEEDED TO TALK TO YOU ABOUT...GOOD LORD... YOUR NEW FORM! YOU'VE CHANGED!

YOU HAVE NO IDEA.
SLUGGY FREELANCE

FWAP!
YIPE!

Gnaw Gnaw
beep!
AYLEE, CALL... ON LINE... TWO.

GWYNN, I TOLD YOU TO HOLD ALL MY CALLS. ALL OF THEM! FOREVER!!!
RIGHT. I'M SORRY, I JUST BUMPED MY HEAD. MAYBE A MINOR CONCUSSION. NOT THINKING STRAIGHT. SORRY.

AYLEE, WAIT! DON'T EAT ME! I'VE GOT SOMETHING IMPORTANT TO TELL YOU!
THIS BETTER BE GOOD.

A MINUTE LATER...
KEE-RASH

WAP
WHUMP ROLL

ALL RIGHT BUDDY. NO UNAUTHORIZED CRASHING THROUGH WINDOWS.
TZZT
TZZT

TORG? TORG!

TORG, ARE YOU OK?
I SAW HER.

I SAW HER! IT WAS HORRIBLE! SHE... WAS HORRIBLE! SHE'S CHANGED FORMS AGAIN, RIFF! ...THE ULTIMATE CEO BOSS. PURE EVIL! AND I DON'T KNOW WHAT SHE'S EATING NOW, BUT I DON'T THINK IT'S POTATOES.

SHE TRIED TO EAT YOU?
SHE WAS GOING TO, I THINK! BUT I TALKED HER OUT OF IT.
WHAT DID YOU TELL HER?
I INVITED HER TO OUR HALLOWEEN PARTY.

AND SHE THREW YOU OUT THE WINDOW? DIDN'T YOU TELL HER ABOUT THE PUMPKIN-CARVING CONTEST? WITH COOL PRIZES?
NO-NO, SHE'S HAPPY TO COME TO THE PARTY! BEING THROWN OUT THE WINDOW WAS HER HAPPY RESPONSE!

YOU'RE VERY LUCKY TO BE ALIVE, TORG. BUT YOU'VE PUT ALL OUR GUESTS IN UN-IMAGINABLE DANGER.

I MEAN, BESIDES THE DANGER THEY'LL BE IN FROM THE DEMON FROM THE DIMENSION OF PAIN WHO COMES BY EVERY HALLOWEEN TO KILL YOU AND CLAIM YOUR SOUL.

IS THERE TIME TO MENTION THE HUNGRY MUTATING SPACE ALIEN ON THE INVITATIONS?
WE'LL MAKE TIME!

This is not an invitation! This is a WARNING! Do not attend Riff and Torg's Halloween party this year! As happens each year, a REAL Demon shall appear to claim the soul of Torg! But this time there will also be a mutating alien who may or may not hunger for YOUR flesh! Dress as unappetizing as possible! Whatever you do, do not attend the party at the date, time and location listed on the back of this warning! -over-
HAPPY HALLOWEEN! NO LIFEGUARD ON DUTY, ENTER AT YOUR OWN RISK!
"RISK" IS RIGHT! IS RIFF GOING TO BE USING THAT DEMON-BLASTER AGAIN THIS YEAR?
I'M AFRAID THE BLASTER IS NOT AVAILABLE TO US THIS YEAR. BUT RIFF HAS DESIGNED A WHOLE NEW DEMON-TRAP!
I'M KIND-OF COUNTING ON DEMONIC INEPTNESS THIS YEAR.
THAT'S WHAT I GET FOR WAITING UNTIL THE LAST MINUTE.
Torg
OOOOH! A LITTLE PLASTIC SQUEEKY-TORG!
IF I HANG TO THE BACK OF THE PARTY, THE DEMON WILL NEVER FIND ME IN THE CROWD. 
ACK!
GOT HIM AGAIN!
YEAH!
ISP AND OSP, YOUR TRAINING HAS PROVEN MOST EFFECTIVE!
YOU'RE TELLING ME!
YOU WILL KILL TORG TONIGHT NO MATTER HOW GREAT HIS DEFENSES!
RIFF, I HAVE TO ADMIT, I DID THINK YOUR SHOEBOX TRAP WOULD BE A MECHA-ION BOX-TRAP OR SOMETHING. BUT IT'S A PLAIN OLD SHOEBOX, STICK, AND STRING! I'M GETTING A LITTLE CONCERNED HERE.
IF THE BOX DOESN'T WORK, WE HIT THE DEMON WITH A LITTLE BANANA CREAM BACKUP.
Torg

GWYNN! GLAD YOU COULD MAKE IT!
I WOULDN'T MISS THE BIGGEST HALLOWEEN PARTY IN TOWN! HOLD MY SPEAR?
WHAM!
THAT'S FOR SPRAYING WINTERGREEN BREATH SPRAY INTO MY EYES, KNOCKING ME OUT, AND STEALING MY KEYCARD!
HEY! RIFF LANDED AN ESCAPE POD ON YOU!
THAT'S WHY SHE GOT TO ME FIRST, TORG. COULD YOU DISLODGE THE TIRE-IRON?

CRYSTAL! HOW'S THE PARTY SO FAR?
WHAT HAPPENED TO YOU GUYS?
GWYNN'S JUST IN A MOOD. NOTHING TO FEAR.
WHERE'S THE BAR? I BROUGHT ONE OF MY **NEW** MIXED DRINKS!
EEYAAAAA!
FUNNY, GUYS.
WHAT IS IT?
MY NEW SPECIAL PIMENTO-OLIVE WINE-COOLER!
HOLY "TURPENWINE", BATMAN!
GOOD GOD CRYSTAL! I THINK THE FUMES ATE HALF MY BRAIN!
THAT'LL STRIP OILS OFF MY CANVASES!

GEE BOSS, ONLY YOU HAVE EYES BIG ENOUGH TO PULL OFF A "TORG" COSTUME.
THE BETTER TO SEE YOU WITH, MY DEAR.
YOU EXPECT US TO BELIEVE THIS BIG THING TO BE TORG?
YOU THOUGHT THE LITTLE THINGY WAS TORG!
A LITTLE TRANSDIMENSIONAL JETLAG. WE'RE BETTER NOW.
Glug Glug
SLUGGY FREELANCE
NOW THAT IS A LADY.
WHY ARE YOU HIDING BACK HERE, TORG?
MOST OF THE DEMONS THAT COME AFTER ME ARE A BIT BUMBLING. BUT THIS YEAR I DON'T HAVE ANY TRICKS UP MY SLEEVE AND RIFF'S GOT NOTHING BUT CREAM PIES.
HAPPY WEEN
WHAT'S WORSE, I REMEMBER HER FROM MY STAY IN THE DIMENSION OF PAIN. SHE'S DOWNRIGHT DANGEROUS. I'VE GOT TO GET OUT OF HERE!
HEAR HIM?
OH YEAH!
CRAP.
TORG'S IN TROUBLE, AND AYLEE ISN'T MOVING TO SAVE HIM THIS TIME! THINK FAST!
WAP!
DID YOU JUST THROW A BANANA CREAM PIE AT MY HEAD?
NO! IT WAS THAT DEMON!
WHAT DEMON?
THE ONE RIGHT OVER... WHERE DID THEY GO?
RIFF! A TRAPDOOR JUST OPENED UP IN THE FLOOR, I DON'T KNOW HOW! THE DEMON AND TORG FELL THROUGH!
WHY DO YOUR HANDS SMELL LIKE BANANAS?
WHAT'S GOING TO GET ME OUT OF THIS ONE?
RIFF, WOULD YOU QUIT THROWING PIES AROUND? WE NEED TO HELP TORG!

RIFF, YOU'VE ALWAYS FEARED MY KIND. ALWAYS WANTED TO DESTROY ME. BUT YOU ARE TOO IN-SIGNIFICANT TO BE A THREAT TO ME. NORMALLY I WOULD JUST KILL YOU. OR IGNORE YOU. BUT YOU ARE JUST SO *DAMN IRRITATING*, YOU DESERVE TO SUFFER.

THAT'S JUST RIFF'S WAY OF SAYING, "I'M SORRY, DON'T EAT MY FRIENDS, AYLEE!"

GEE, LOOK AT THE TIME...

"FROM THE MANTLE. I COULD SWEAR THAT WAS A GHOST'S ARM! ANGELA'S RIGHT. THIS PLACE *IS* HAUNTED."

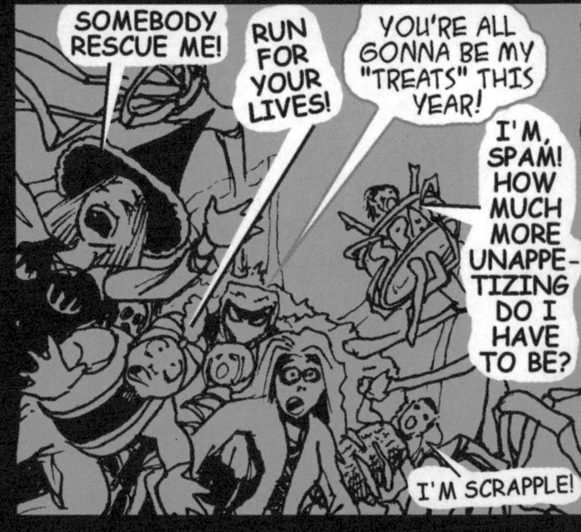

SOUNDS LIKE THE PARTY'S HOPPING UP THERE. AND THE ONLY COMPANY I HAVE IS THIS GLOW-NECKLACE. I THINK I'LL CALL YOU WILSON. NONE OF MY FRIENDS HAVE COME DOWN FOR ME, AND THE DEMON HASN'T COME UP FOR ME, WILSON. CAN'T WAIT HERE FOREVER.

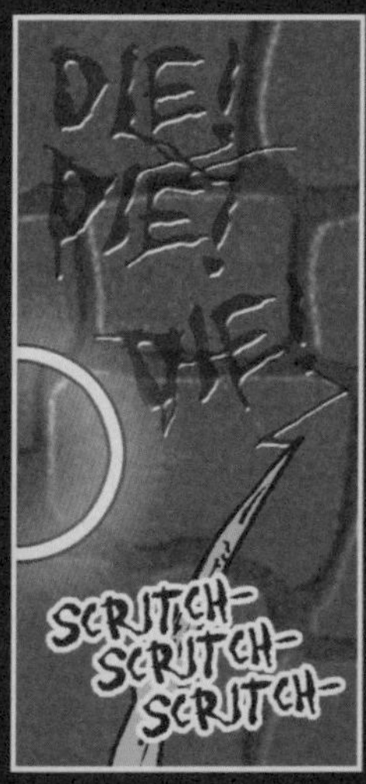

GWYNN! HELP! AYLEE IS HURTING PEOPLE AND I WANT HER TO STOP, BUT I CAN'T FIND HER TO TALK TO HER. SHE'LL LISTEN TO YOU!
SHE'S OUTSIDE, KIKI. AND I DON'T CARE WHAT SHE'S DOING.
Doing

KIKI, PIPE DOWN. AYLEE'S GOT NO BEEF WITH GWYNN, SINCE GWYNN WORKS FOR HER, AND WE'RE OFF THE MENU. WE'RE ALL SAFE HERE.
BUT EVERYBODY ELSE IS GETTING HURT! WHAT ABOUT HELPING THEM?

KIKI, GWYNN AND I ARE ALIKE IN ONE WAY. THERE'S ONLY ONE PERSON ON THIS PLANET THAT WE TRULY CARE ABOUT.

OURSELVES.
I WAS GOING TO SAY "ME".

FINE. DON'T TALK TO ME. I'LL JUST TWIDDLE MY THUMBS UNTIL DAWN WHEN YOU RETURN TO YOUR OWN DIMENSION.

MAYBE YOU'LL TALK TO HAPPY-WILSON-GLOW-MOUTH!
ARE YOU ENJOYING THE PARTY TONIGHT?
KILL TORG
SCRITCH-SCRITCH

WHY DO YOU WANT TO KILL TORG?
WANT GO HOME
ORDERD KILL TORG
SCRITCH-SCRITCH-SCRITCH

WHAT'S YOUR NAME?
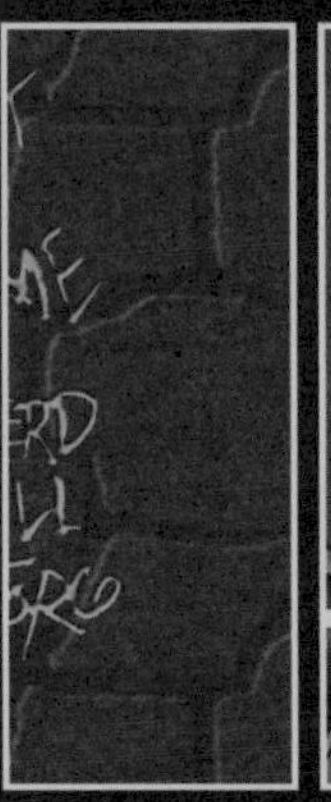

COME ON. THAT'S SUPPOSED TO BE AN EASY ONE. WHEN YOU ARRIVED YOU SAID IT WAS ORBZ OR SPRITZ OR...
"MOSP"? NICE NAME. I'D MAKE FUN OF IT, BUT MY NAME'S TORG!
MOSP
SCRITCH-SCRITCH

WHAT ARE YOU DOING, GWYNN? PUTTING YOUR LIFE ON THE LINE FOR YOUR UN-GRATEFUL "FRIENDS". AGAIN. I DON'T EVEN KNOW IF AYLEE WILL LISTEN TO ME. I MISS ZOË.

WHAT'S AYLEE DOING IN THE BACKYARD?

OH HOLY GOD.

GWYNN, WE NEED TO DISCUSS THE IMPORTANCE OF COMPANY LOYALTY.

NOOOOOOO!

BLAM!
BLAM!
BLAM!
BLAM!
BLAM!
BLAM!

I HAD HER BUT SHE TURNED THE CORNER TOO QUICK! SOMEONE WAS WITH HER! HOW CAN SOMETHING THAT BIG SKITTER THAT FAST?
SHE'S NOT THAT FAST, SHE'S...

THUMP!

...ON THE ROOF!
SLUGGY FREELANCE

I GUESS THE WINDOW IT IS.

geez. It's like they've never seen a *howdy kitten* costume before!

YOU'RE SUPPOSED TO BE A KITTEN?

OK, MOSP. IT LOOKS LIKE THIS DEBRIS IS NOT ONLY PINNING YOU, BUT IT'S ALSO BLOCKING A PASSAGE OUT OF THIS PIT. YOU JUST HAVE TO PROMISE TO NOT KILL ME AND STUFF.

DUH, ME! WILSON SAYS I SHOULD JUST WAIT UNTIL DAWN WHEN YOU POOF AWAY AND I'LL BE SAFE TO CLEAR THE WAY OUT!

MOSP?

MOSP? ARE YOU OK? **MOSP?**

SHUT UP, WILSON.
PRY!

WHAT A DISASTER. I'M GOING TO NEED ANOTHER COSTUME IF I'M GOING TO SNEAK...
AND WHAT ARE YOU DOING HERE, IRVING?

KUSARI?
YESSSS.
WHY, NOTHING AT ALL! JUST ENJOYING A HALLOWEEN PARTY THROWN BY SOME FRIENDS!

NOT HERE TO TALK TO ANYONE? YES? WE CAN TRUST YOU, CAN'T WE?
KUSARI, WITH AYLEE ATTACKING ANYTHING THAT MOVES, I FIGURE I ONLY HAVE A TEN PERCENT CHANCE OF SURVIVAL! I JUST WANT TO GET OUT OF HERE ALIVE!

THEN LET US LEAVE THIS PLACE TOGETHER.
THERE GOES MY TEN PERCENT.

I SAY WE MAKE A BREAK FOR IT! THE ALIEN CAN'T EAT US ALL!

HEY LOOK! "PROUD TO INFORM YOU"...BLA, BLA, BLA...
HEY! WE WON THE BEST COSTUME CONTEST!
WHAT DO WE WIN?

YANK!

YEARGH!
I NEVER WIN NUTHIN'!

WELL, I CLEARED A WAY THROUGH THE PASSAGE THAT I HOPE LEADS OUT. I CLEARED ENOUGH DEBRIS OFF YOU. YOU SHOULD BE FINE UNTIL DAWN, WHICH SHOULD BE COMING SOON.

BURLP! BELCH!
OHHH
EASY THERE, DEMON. DIDN'T MIND THE DEMONIC PASSING-OUT, BUT I DON'T WANNA SEE WHAT A DEMON HANGOVER LOOKS LIKE!

ACTUALLY WE ARE IMPERVIOUS TO HANGOVERS!

JUST NEEDED A NAP IS ALL!
DIE!
STAB!

WILSON THE GLOW-NECKLACE DEFLECTED THE IMPALING ATTACK THAT WOULD HAVE KILLED ME! YOU SAVED MY LIFE WILSON! I'LL TRY TO MAKE IT A LIFE YOU'D BE PROUD OF!
NICE GLOW-NECKLACE!
SINCE WE'RE GONNA STAB YOU THROUGH THE HEAD WITH OUR OTHER SPEAR-ARM, YOU MIGHT WANT TO RETHINK THE WHOLE "WILSON NOT DYING IN VAIN" THING.

RIFF, I JUST SAW SOMETHING...
SHHHH! HEAR THAT?
WHAT?
THE QUIET.

THERE'S NOBODY LEFT?
I'M COMING FOR YOU RIFF. PREPARE YOURSELF

WE NEED TO HIT HER WITH EVERYTHING WE GOT. WHAT'S OUR INVENTORY?
BESIDES THE GUNS WE'RE CARRYING? A SHOEBOX, STICK, AND STRING. AND A BANANA CREAM PIE.
TRICK OR TREAT

PLAN B. I EAT THE PIE AND YOU RUN LIKE CRAZY.

MOSP, PLEASE DON'T KILL ME! I THOUGHT WE WERE FRIENDS!

DID HE JUST CALL US A COUPLE OF MOPS?
WHO IS **MOSP**? WE ARE **ISP** AND **OSP**, AND YOUR INACCURACY OFFENDS US!

YEAH, WE'RE ALL REALLY PISSED NOW!
MOSP IS SUCH A STUPID NAME! SEE YOU BACK IN HELL, MORTAL SCUM!

WELL? ARE YOU GOING TO IMPALE HIM?
ME? I THOUGHT **YOU** WORKED THE ARMS!

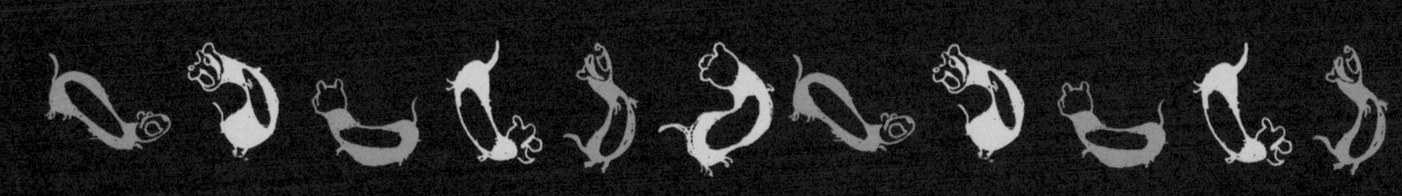

WHY CAN'T WE MOVE, ISP? FLAMING REAKK ON A BAGEL, WHAT IS GOING ON HERE?
I CAN'T BELIEVE THEY DON'T EVEN ACKNOWLEDGE YOU. I'M SORRY MOSP.

SILENCE, MORTAL! MEET DOUBLE SPEARING DEATHHHHHH!

RAIN CHECK ON THE DOUBLE SPEARING DEATHHHHHH!
I CAN NIP HIS NOSE IF HE GETS A TINY BIT CLOSER!
nip
nip
nip

MAN, THIS MOSP THING IS A REAL INCONVENIENCE!
EEK! THE DAWN! HOW ARE WE GOING TO EXPLAIN THI...*
SEE YOU NEXT YEAR?
POOF

THIS IS YOUR BEST EFFORT, RIFF? YOU HAVE TO BE KIDDING.
ALIEN FOOD
ALIEN FOOD

WAIT. THIS ISN'T STRING! IT'S WIRE!

SASHA! HIT IT!

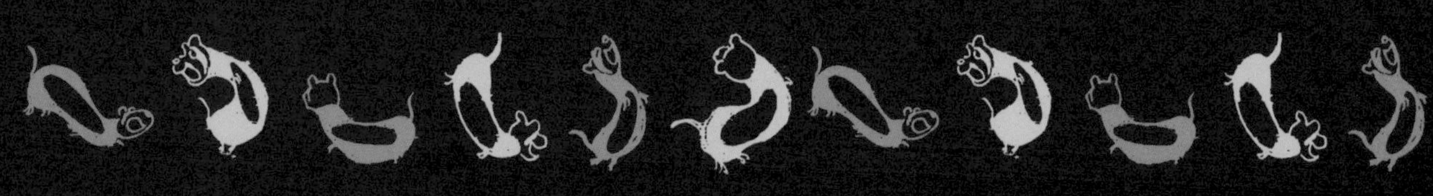

HOPE YOUR NEW FORM ISN'T AS SHOCK-FRIENDLY AS YOUR LAST ONE!
ZAPPO!

ZAPPO!
ZAPPO!

ZAPPO!
ZAPPO!
ZAPPO!

RIFF! WE BLEW A GRID WITH THAT! BUT IT WORKED!
SNAP
SHAKE

RIFF? ARE YOU OK?

RIFF?

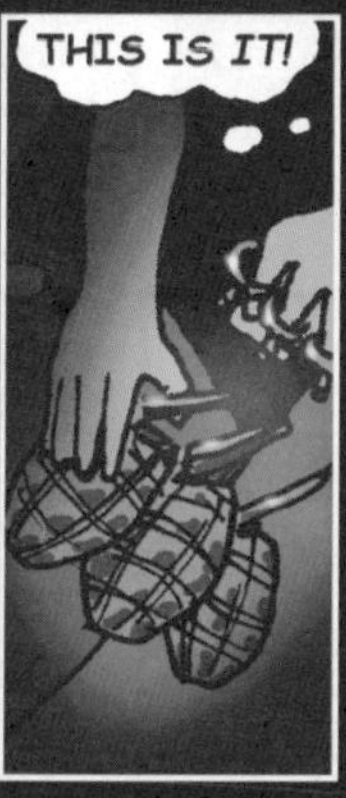

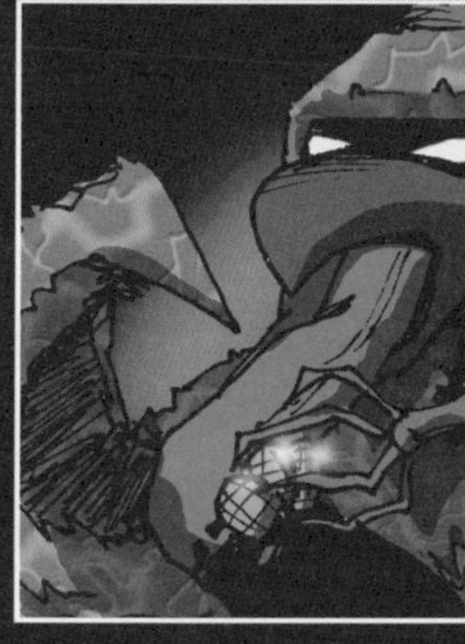

I THINK I CAN GET THESE PINS BACK IN. I'M RATHER DEXTEROUS WHEN IT COMES TO THE SMALL THINGS.

"DO YOU THINK I COULD MAKE SIXTY PEOPLE DISAPPEAR AT ONE TIME IN ONE PLACE WITHOUT SOMEBODY NOTICING? I'M MORE DISCREET FOR THE TIME BE-ING. LUCKILY I DON'T HAVE TO DEVOUR YOU AND ALL YOUR FRIENDS TO BREAK YOUR SPIRIT. I HAVE PROVEN THAT I CAN KILL YOU ALL AT WILL."

"YOU KNOW HOW IT FEELS TO BE POWERLESS. TO BE ON THE VERGE OF DEATH. TO FAIL YOUR FRIENDS. HOLD ON TO THAT. BOTTOM LINE, IF YOU OR ANY OF YOUR FRIENDS INTERFERE IN MY BUSINESS AGAIN, I'LL PUT AWAY MY 'KID GLOVES.'"

YOU GUYS HAVE BEEN IN HERE PLAYING VIDEO GAMES THIS WHOLE TIME?
WHAT OF IT?

DIDN'T YOU EVEN *CONSIDER* HELPING THE GUESTS WHO WERE BEING ATTACKED BY AYLEE? OR ME, TRAPPED IN THE BASEMENT WITH A DEMON?
I DID... *A LITTLE*, THEN I FORGOT.
woof.

AS PUNISHMENT, YOU HAVE TO GIVE UP THE CONTROLLER.
AW, MAN.
HERE COMES A NEW CHALLENGER!
wuf.

SINCE WHEN DO YOU HAVE TIME TO PLAY VIDEO GAMES?
MY GIRLFRIEND IS CHEMICALLY PARALYZED!*

* TECHNICALLY OUT OF CHARACTER. GIRLFRIEND OR NOT, TORG *ALWAYS* HAS TIME FOR VIDEO GAMES!
-The Management.

HOW ARE YOU FEELING?
LIKE MY HEAD IS IN A VISE.

BUT IT'S NOT.
NO.

SO YOU HAVE ALL THE SUFFERING, BUT NONE OF THE COOL FEATURES OF *ACTUALLY* HAVING A VISE ON YOUR HEAD.

THIS SUCKS.
WOULDN'T IT BE COOL IF I HAD A LATHE FOR AN ARM?
YOU'VE BEEN NIPPING INTO THE HALLOWEEN CANDY, HAVEN'T YOU?

THANKS GUYS. THAT STUNT YOU PULLED ALMOST GOT ME FIRED.
STUNT *WE* PULLED? YOU CAN'T BE SERIOUS.

YOU TRIED TO KILL AYLEE! IN THE END SHE DIDN'T KILL ANYBODY.
GWYNN, THAT'S NOT FAIR. AYLEE SCARED A LOT OF PEOPLE.
SO SHE ACTED SCARY! IT WAS HALLOWEEN! THE WAY YOU GUYS RESPONDED WITH REAL WEAPONS, IT'S NO SURPRISE THAT THIS WAS YOUR LAST HALLOWEEN PARTY.
GUYS! EVERYONE'S ALREADY R.S.V.P'D FOR NEXT YEAR! WE'RE BEING BILLED AS THE MOST EXCITING AND REALISTIC SCI-FI ADAPTATION OF "HOW TO HOST A MURDER" EVER! EVENT OF THE YEAR, TWO YEARS RUNNING! WE'RE GOING TO HAVE TO START TURNING PEOPLE AWAY, AND IT'S NOT UNTIL NEXT YEAR!

I DON'T SUPPOSE YOU CAN SQUEEZE *MY* NAME ON THAT LIST?
DON'T HURT ME.

IN ANY CASE, OUTSIDE OF RIFF'S DEPRESSION AND ANGELA BEING SLIGHTLY MORE JITTERY THAN USUAL, EVERYTHING'S JUST ABOUT GOTTEN BACK TO NORMAL AROUND HERE! OH, PLUS WE HAVE A GHOST IN THE HOUSE! HOW WAS YOUR HALLOWEEN, ZOË?

IT WAS FUN!

BEFORE WE BEGIN THIS MEETING, I WANT EVERYONE TO MEET MY NEW PERSONAL ATTACHÉ. EVERYONE? KILLUM.
HELLO.

YOU... UM...WANT US TO KILL HIM, SIR?
NO-NO, ROBERTS. THAT IS HIS NAME. "MR. KILLUM". HE USED TO RUN WITH GENERAL MAYHEM'S BOYS, AND YOU KNOW HOW PRETENTIOUS THEY ARE ABOUT NAMES. IN ANY CASE, THIS MEETING HAS TO DO WITH SOME QUESTIONS WE HAVE FOR KIRKO.
SLUGGY FREELANCE

I'LL BEGIN. DR. KIRKO, WHY IS IT OUR MOST VALUABLE DISCOVERY WAS ALLOWED TO MARCH AROUND IN PUBLIC AND GO TO A HALLOWEEN PARTY? JEOPARDIZING THE INTEGRITY OF OUR BIGGEST PROJECT?
DAN-MET

YOU WANTED HER UNSTOPPABLE. WE MADE HER UNSTOPPABLE. AND NOW YOU EXPECT US TO STOP HER? GET IT STRAIGHT, SISTER. AYLEE IS NOT WHAT'S VALUABLE TO US. THE ABILITY TO GENERATE AN ARMY OF HER KIND AT WILL IS, AND WE'RE CLOSE.
KIRKO

I SHARE DAN-MET'S CONCERNS. I REMEMBER THE LAST TIME WE HAD A SECURITY ISSUE INVOLVING CLONING. THE PERCY PROJECT, I BELIEVE. WE ALL REMEMBER WHAT A DISASTER THAT WAS.
DAN-MET
CHEN
ROBERTS

NEED I REMIND YOU THE WOOLLY MAMMOTH CLONING ITSELF WAS A SUCCESS? UNLIKE YOUR RETRIEVAL OF THE OASIS PROJECT, CHEN.
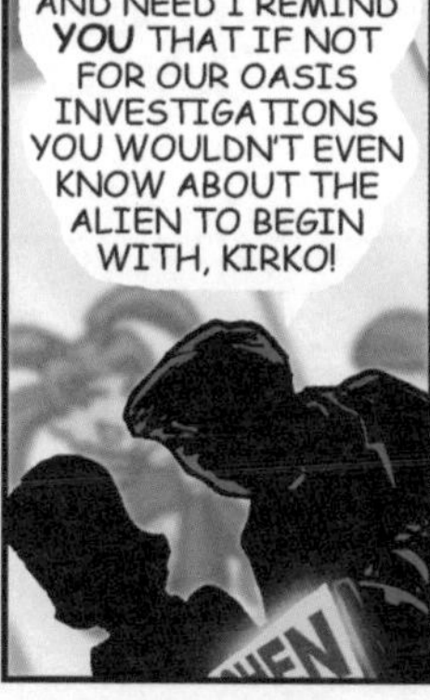
AND NEED I REMIND YOU THAT IF NOT FOR OUR OASIS INVESTIGATIONS YOU WOULDN'T EVEN KNOW ABOUT THE ALIEN TO BEGIN WITH, KIRKO!

WHAT I WANT TO KNOW IS WHAT WAS IRVING SCHLOCK DOING THERE? KUSARI?

UNIMPORTANT. DR. SCHLOCK IS EASILY MOTIVATED BY FEAR, THUS EASY FOR US TO CONTROL. HIS INFORMATION IS STILL VALUABLE TO US.
KUSARI

I DON'T TRUST HIM. AS SOON AS HE STOPS BEING AN ASSET, KILL HIM.

YES?
"YES" WHAT?
KILLUM

WHAT DO YOU WANT ME TO DO AS SOON AS HE STOPS HELPING?
I SAID, "KILL HIM". NOT "KILLUM"! DAMN IT!
KILLUM

YES?
DAN-MET

I WANT UPDATES ON THE OASIS PROJECT! CHEN?

ONE TRACER AND TRANSPONDER IN PLACE, BUT MY NEWS IS TROUBLING.
HOLD UP! I DROPPED MY KEYS AND CAN'T FIND THEM. I'M GOING TO HAVE TO TURN ON THE LIGHTS.
CLICK!
CHEN
ROBERTS

OWWW!
YOU JERK, ROBERTS!
YEAAAH!
JEEZ!
GOT 'EM!
HEY!
CLICK!

NOW I HAVE TO SPEND THE REST OF THE MEETING SEEING SPOTS. NO TURNING ON THE LIGHTS IN THE EVIL ROOM DAMMIT!

SOH-OH-OH-RY! SHEESH, WHAT A WHINER!
WHAT DID I DO?
DAN-MET

YOU DARE...?
KILL HIM!

YES? WHAT?
SIGH
KILLUM

RIFF and the jellyfish sucker 2001
JELLYFISH SUCKER 2001

THE EVENTS IN THIS STORY PRECEDE THOSE IN THE REST OF THIS BOOK. (WHO KNEW?)
THIS IS MUNCHEEN WALNUTS HERE FOR GUAC-8-NEWS ON OUR LITTLE VACATION PLANET OF CHAU-5!
OUR BLOOD-TREATY WITH THE ZORGONS IS OFFICIAL! AS GRAVY ON THE DEAL, THE NOBLE RULER OF THE ZORGONS, ZORGON GOLA, IS HERE TO PRESENT A BATTLECRUISER TO OUR LEADER VACADO THE GUACAN!
GUAC-8-NEWS
WE HAVE AN ALLIANCE! LET'S SHAKE ON IT.
PUT 'ER THERE, PAL!
LIVE FEED
I MEAN THERE! OF COURSE I DO!
LIVE FEED [yum]
AT THE HELM, CAPTAIN JIMMY DEAN BACKBACON, THE NATIONAL HERO FROM THE BATTLE AT SHISH KABOB POINT!
WHO BETTER TO INSPIRE CONFIDENCE IN THE CREW AS THEY PREPARE THE FIRST DEEP SPACE BATTLE-CRUISER IN GUACAN HISTORY TO LEAVE ORBIT!
AND CAPTAIN BACKBACON AND CREW AREN'T THE ONLY ONES ON THIS HISTORICAL LAUNCH! FIFTY TOURISTS ARE JOINING THEM! BECAUSE ON CHAU-5, VACATIONERS FROM OTHER WORLDS COME FIRST COURSE.
...I MEAN, "FIRST, OF COURSE!" ALTHOUGH THEY'RE BEING KEPT IN CUPBOARDS, WE'RE NOT GOING TO EAT 'EM!
OBSERVATION DECK
HELP!
OF COURSE NOT, MUNCHEEN! HERE ON CHAU-5 WE DON'T EAT PEOPLE!

GUACANS IN SPAAAACE!

A PUNYVERSE STORY

ZOOMFOOSHZIP!
WELL, OUR NEW "ZOOMFOOSHZIP" DRIVE WORKS!
HEY! I CALLED SNACK BREAK! WHO'S PUSHING STUFF?

LATER:
MMMMMMMM. THAT SNACK WAS GREAT! I MEAN, I'M SURE THE TOURISTS ENJOYED THEIR SNACK. NESS. BUT NOW MAYBE WE SHOULD STOP WITH THE QUICK-MOVING-THINGY-AND-STUFF.

WAK
WAK
WAK

NO GOOD. WON'T STOP.
LOOKOUT! PLANET!

WAK
GNAW

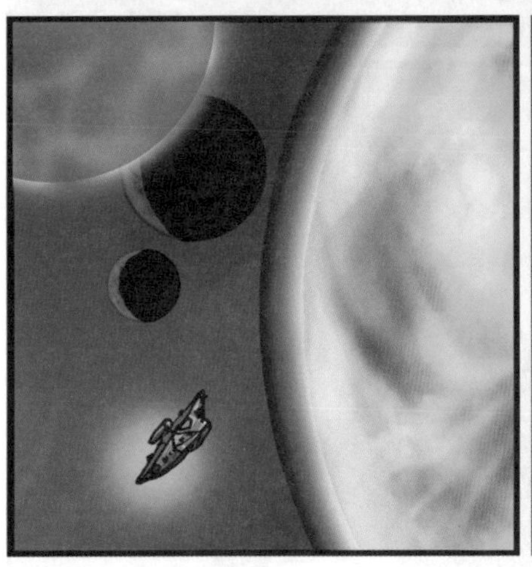

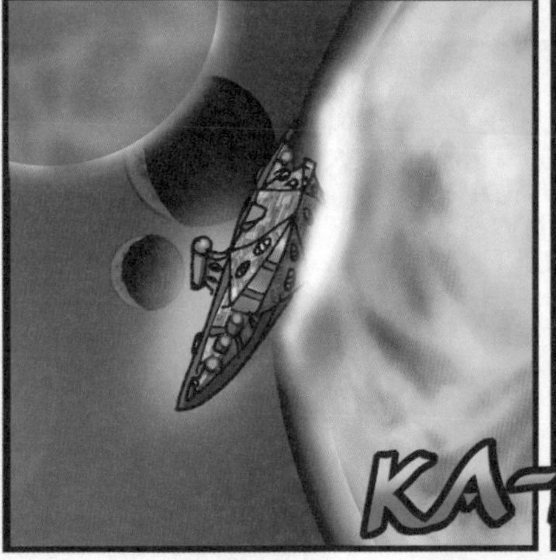

KA-RUNCH!

THAT'S NOT GOOD! DAMAGE REPORT?

OUR OUTER HULL HAS BEEN SEARED NICELY TO SEAL IN THE JUICES, AND GARNISHED DELICATELY WITH PLANETSIDE VEGETATION.

TOURIST LUNCH BREAK!

PARADISIA
LOHVO HOMEWORLD

KING LOHVO PROAN, A ZORGON SHIP HAS JUST ATTACKED THE PEACEFUL PLANET OF HOOCAIRS-3!
GET ME GOFOTRON!

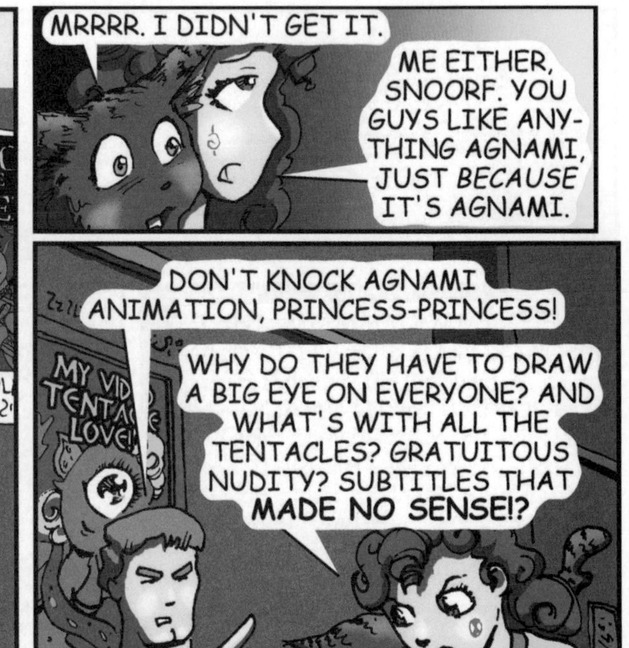

ERT! ERT! ERT!

THERE WERE SUBTITLES? THE GOFOTRON ALARM! SOMEBODY'S IN PERIL!

QUICK! WHILE NO ONE'S WATCHING!

GO-GO-GOFOTRON!

CLICK!

NOW PLAYING: [1] MY VIDEO TENTACLE LOVE!
OHVO TITLES [2] GOLA 1/2
UP, UP, AND UP MORE!
‹WHAT WERE THEY COMPLAINING ABOUT?›
‹LIKE *ANYTHING* IS CAMPIER THAN "GOFOTRON".›
SLAY-R
‹YOU KNOW THEIR PROBLEM? NO TENTACLES!›

HAS EX-LORD HUHBUTBUT BEEN DEALT WITH?
VACADO THE GUACAN IS HAVING HIM OVER FOR DINNER AS WE SPEAK. WE HAVE REPORTS THAT **GOFOTRON** HAS BEEN DISPATCHED TO DEAL WITH THE **ZF GOLABOLA.**
WE HAVE TO REACH THE ZF GOLA-BOLA FIRST, ADVISOR WURDOP. HAVE OUR NEAREST SHIP DISPATCHED.
THAT WOULD BE THE **ZF BUMBLER,** PILOTED BY **CAPTAIN FETTUH GRATER**, MY LORD.

DO YOU FEEL *ANYTHING?* EVEN A *LITTLE* TICKLE?
MY THROAT STILL FEELS FINE CAPTAIN GRATER **SIR!** URGENT MESSAGE FROM ZORGON COMMAND, **SIR!**
I'M SQUISHING YOUR HEAD!
DULY NOTED, **SIR!**

AN AMAZINGLY SHORT TIME LATER IN THE HOOCAIRS SYSTEM...
HALT, ZORGON SCUM!
DO'H!

CAPTAIN! IT'S GOFOTRON! WHAT SHOULD WE DO?
WE COULD COOK IT! NOT THAT WE'D EAT IT OR ANYTHING.

THE CAPTAIN WANTS TO KNOW IF WE HAVE A RECIPE FOR GIANT ROBOTS OF JUSTICE.
GALLEY
LET ME CHECK MY THROATS.

ARE WE GOING TO WAIT AROUND ALL DAY?
THE MESSAGE FROM THE ZORGON BATTLE CRUISER IS THAT THEY NEED TO "PREHEAT" TO ENSURE EVEN COOKING.
ROOT- ROOT- RECIPE?
DON'T LIKE THE SNOORF OF THAT. LET'S SNOORF RIGHT TO "COOL MOVE THAT WINS BATTLE".

GOFOTRON-COOL-MOVE-THAT-WINS-BATTLE-
HA!

chop-it-to-me!

ARE WE WINNING?
ALMOST!

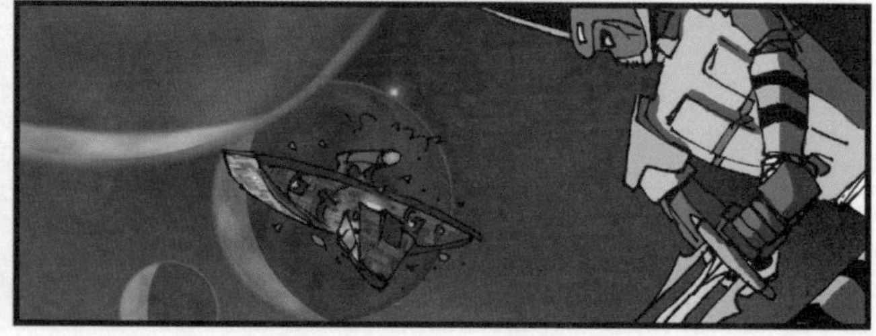

THE SHIP IS GOING DOWN! ABANDON SHIP!!!
OH NO! DUE TO POOR PLANNING THERE ARE ONLY ENOUGH LIFE-BOATS FOR THE RICH!
WE WON'T EAT U
GAK!
GLAD THAT WORKED! EVERYONE ELSE TO THE ESCAPE PODS!

LAUNCHING ESCAPE PODS NOW!

SHOULDN'T WE BE IN THEM FIRST?

RETURNING ESCAPE PODS NOW!

LAUNCHING ESCAPE PODS NOW!
MUCH BETTER.

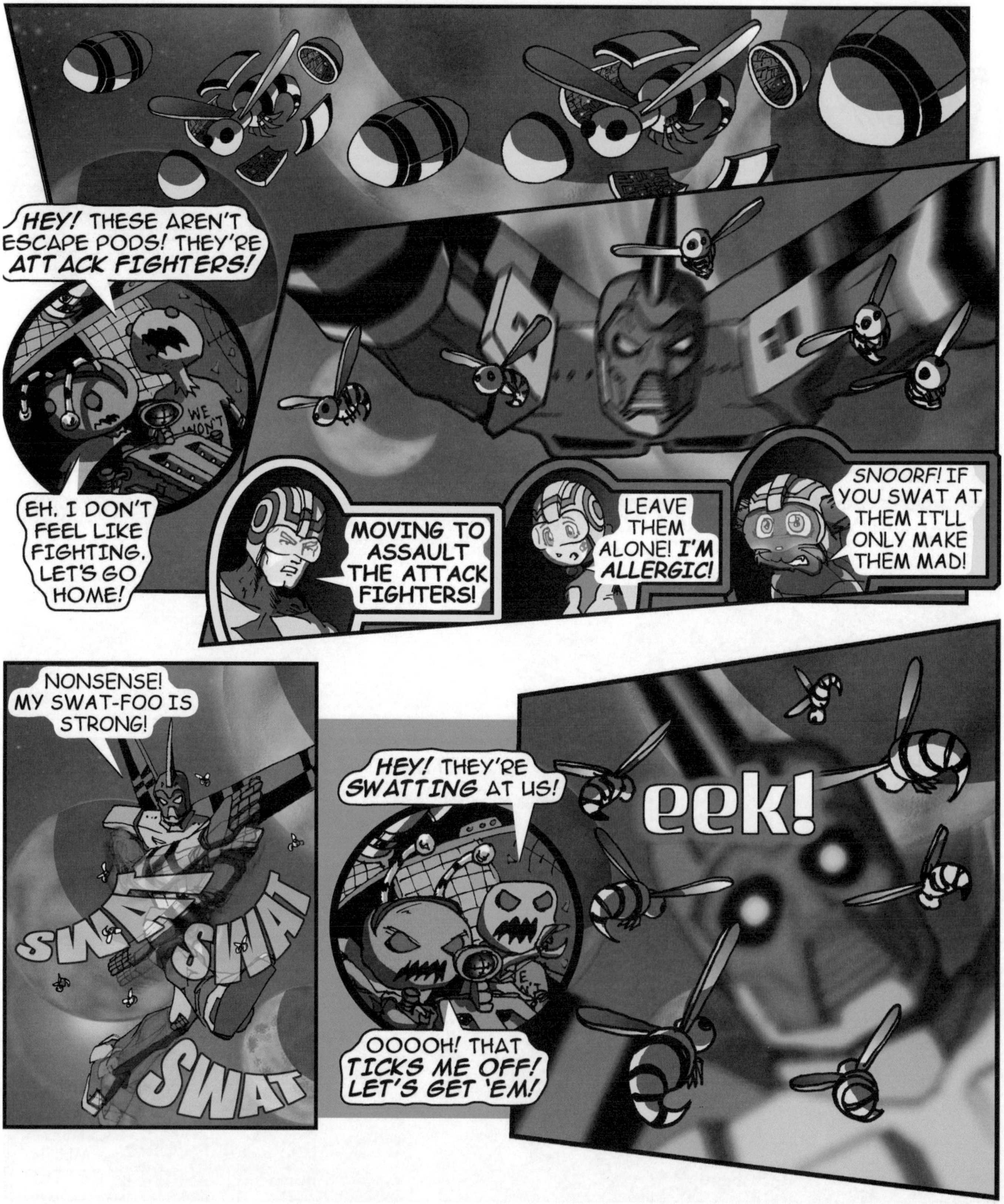

HEY! THESE AREN'T ESCAPE PODS! THEY'RE ATTACK FIGHTERS!

EH. I DON'T FEEL LIKE FIGHTING. LET'S GO HOME!

MOVING TO ASSAULT THE ATTACK FIGHTERS!

LEAVE THEM ALONE! I'M ALLERGIC!

SNOORF! IF YOU SWAT AT THEM IT'LL ONLY MAKE THEM MAD!

EEK!
DON'T LET THEM GET IN MY HAIR!
OW! OW!
OW!

THERE'S GOFOTRON, CAPTAIN GRATER!
ASSUME "ALL THAT" POSITION... IS HE RUNNING AWAY?

THIS UNPRECEDENTED EXCLUSIVE GALACTIC SATELLITE FOOTAGE CLEARLY SHOWS GOFOTRON **FLEEING** BEFORE A ZORGON BATTLECRUISER LAST ZORGON WEEKFALL! WHAT CAPTAIN COULD INSTILL SUCH FEAR IN OUR NOBLE GOFOTRON?

WHY NONE OTHER THAN THE NEWLY APPOINTED COMMANDING GENERAL OF THE ZORGON ARMIES, A MAN THE LOHVOS KNOW ONLY AS... ***LORD GRATER!***

SORRY FOR PERMANENTLY HIDEOUSLY SCARRING YOUR FACE WHEN WE PUT THE TOO-HOT MASK ON.
YEAOUCH! BUT IT HAPPENS!

ZORGON GOLA, I SHALL BE YOURS UNTIL THE END OF THE UNIVERSE! HEY, NICE BIRTHMARK!

ADVISOR WURDOP, ARE YOU SURE THIS IS SUCH A GOOD IDEA?
IT'S THAT, OR ADMIT IT WAS THE GUACANS WHO ROUTED GOFOTRON. BETTER FOR THE PEOPLE TO HAVE A HERO. BY THE WAY, THE GUACANS ARE DEMANDING MORE TECHNOLOGY TO REPLACE THE DESTROYED BATTLECRUISER.
THIS TIME LET'S JUST GIVE THEM LASER-FOILS.

THE END.

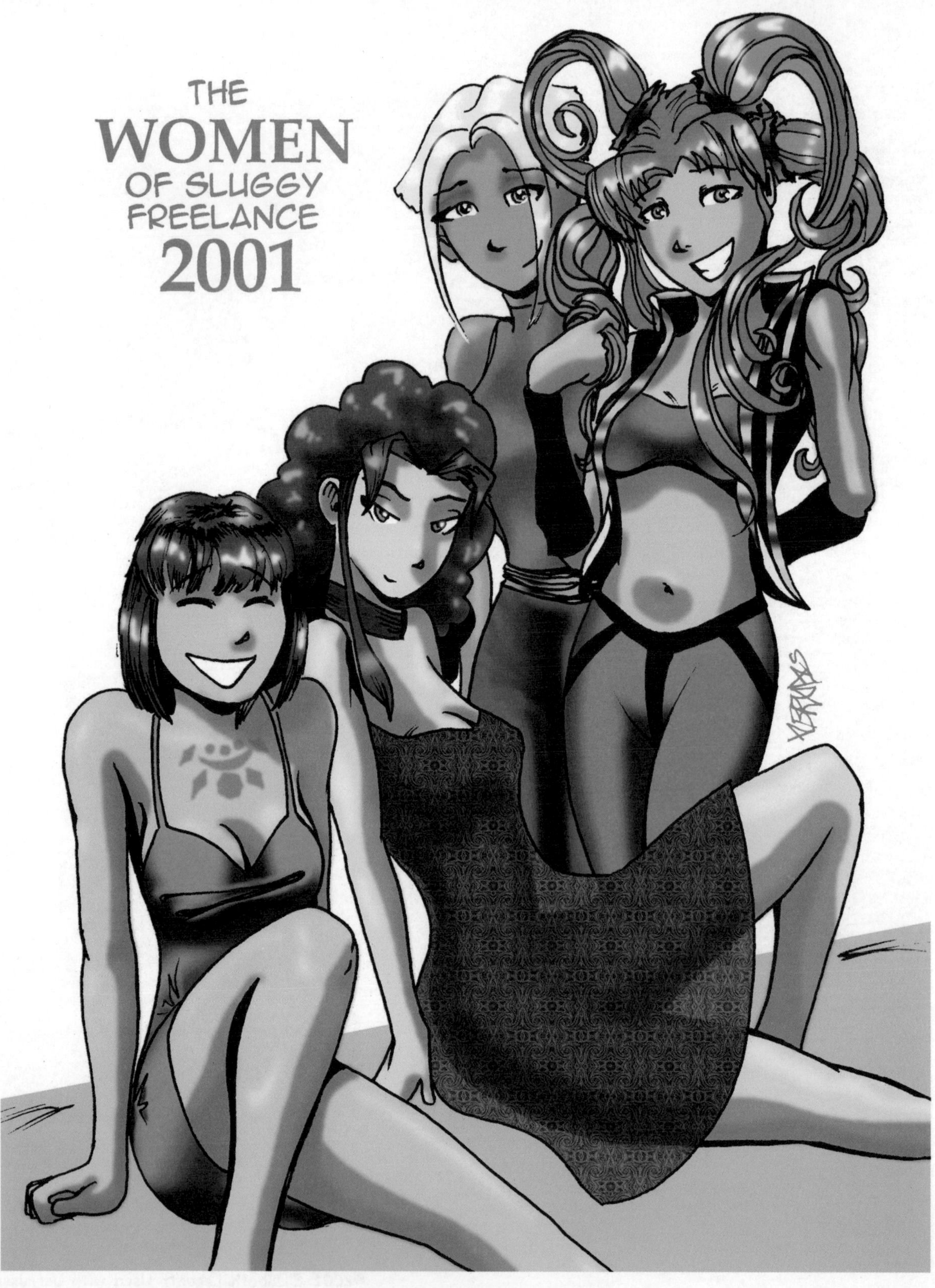
THE
WOMEN
OF SLUGGY
FREELANCE
2001